D0651910

JAMES HUTTON —THE FOUNDER OF MODERN GEOLOGY

James Hutton —the Founder of Modern Geology

by

EDWARD BATTERSBY BAILEY
F.R.S., F.R.S.E.
Formerly, Director of the Geological Survey of Great Britain
Professor of Geology, University of Glasgow

With a Foreword by

J. E. Richey, F.R.S., F.R.S.E.
Queen's College, Dundee,
University of St. Andrews, Scotland

ELSEVIER PUBLISHING CO. LTD.

AMSTERDAM — LONDON — NEW YORK

1967

ELSEVIER PUBLISHING CO. LTD.
BARKING, ESSEX, ENGLAND

ELSEVIER PUBLISHING CO.
335 JAN VAN GALENSTRAAT
P.O. BOX 211, AMSTERDAM

AMERICAN ELSEVIER PUBLISHING COMPANY INC.
52 VANDERBILT AVENUE
NEW YORK, N.Y.

Library of Congress Catalog Card No. 66-28574

Printed by Galliard Limited, Great Yarmouth, England

FOREWORD

Sir Edward Bailey was well fitted to write a commentary on the fundamental work which Dr. James Hutton carried out during the second half of the 18th century. Bailey had already written notable essays on Hutton's life and work, especially in "Edinburgh's Place in Scientific Progress", a book compiled for the British Association Meeting in that city in 1921, and in the series published in 1948 by the Royal Society of Edinburgh at the time of the 150th anniversary of Hutton's death. The present work, in contrast, makes available for the first time Hutton's 3-volume work setting out amongst other subjects his Theory of the Earth in a useful and attractive form for present-day readers.

Shortly after Hutton's death his somewhat obscure writings were clarified and extended by his friend, Professor John Playfair of Edinburgh, in the book "Illustrations of the Huttonian Theory". Bailey's contribution in the present volume is of a different kind and value. Indeed not a single illustration was included with the author's manuscript at the time of his death, and he has used only the written word, including extracts taken *seriatim* from Hutton's volumes, in Hutton's own words where his observations and deductions were expressed with clarity, or re-expressed where the original verbiage was overlengthy or obscure in its meaning. In addition Bailey has supplied throughout, a commentary on Hutton's deductions which perhaps only Bailey with his personal knowledge of Scotland and parts of Europe to which Hutton has referred could have made with such confidence and consideration. He, too, has brought insight into the difficulties of many fundamental geological problems recognised by Hutton, and appreciation of the intelligence and Scottish power of argument which Hutton applied in his deductions. Hutton too not only laid the foundations of the science by his observations in Scotland but in his comments upon the work of his contemporaries in Europe, especially de Saussure in the Swiss Alps, utilised and corrected points of view of his time.

It is none-the-less in Bailey's assessments that Huttonian theory is brought up to date, providing a comprehensive and readable account of the great master's work. In Bailey's writings as a commentator we find especial pleasure and profit, and he may be said to have made in this, his final task, his own greatest contribution, apart from his own achievements, to furthering the progress of science. His manner of elucidating and re-expressing in vivid, inspiring language results achieved by others, taking them many stages further on the road to final solutions, has in no other case been more usefully applied than in his treatment of Hutton's Theory of the Earth.

It was a matter of regret that this book in its final form had only just been completed at Bailey's death, but it is a satisfaction now to find that his last wishes are being fulfilled and this book made available for others to read.

Bailey, of all men of science, would I am sure agree with a quotation from Byron:

> "All who joy would win
> Must share it—Happiness was born a twin".

J.E.R.

PUBLISHERS' NOTE

EDWARD BATTERSBY BAILEY was a former Director of the Geological Survey of Great Britain and the Museum of Practical Geology, also for a time Professor of Geology in the University of Glasgow. He was born on 1 July 1881 and died on 19 March 1965, having dedicated his life to geological thinking and exposition. Though his studies extended beyond the confines of the United Kingdom and over a wide range of geology, his major work was interpretation, into three-dimensional concepts, of the phenomena observed by surface mapping of mainly igneous and metamorphic rocks in the mountains, hills and islands of western Scotland. His work was marked by physical and mental fearlessness and enthusiasm, reinforced by a flair or instinct for arriving at a novel explanation of his own or others' observations.

In addition to his awards for gallantry in the years of the first war and his knighthood, Bailey received many honours. He was elected a Fellow of the Royal Society in 1930, he served on the Council from 1943–1945 and was a Vice-President in 1945; he received a Royal Medal in 1943. He was elected a foreign member of the Norwegian Academy of Science and Letters in 1938; honorary fellow of the National Institute of Sciences of India in 1941; foreign associate of the National Academy of Sciences, Washington, in 1944; associate of the Royal Academy of Belgium in 1946; and honorary member of the Swiss Academy of Sciences in 1948.

He received honorary degrees from the following universities: S.D. Harvard 1936; D.Sc. Birmingham 1939; LL.D. Glasgow 1946; D.Sc. Belfast 1946; Sc.D. Cambridge 1952 and D.Sc. Edinburgh 1964. He was an honorary fellow of Clare College, Cambridge.

From the Royal Society of Edinburgh he received the Neill Prize for 1929 and from the Geological Society of London, the Wollaston Fund (1910), the Bigsby (1923), Murchison (1935) and Wollaston (1948) medals. From the Edinburgh Geological Society in 1962 he received the Clough Medal founded to honour his former chief.

Extracted from "Bibliographical Memoirs of Fellows of the Royal Society", Vol. 11, 1965. Reprinted by permission of the author Sir James Stubblefield and the Royal Society.

CONTENTS

Chapter 1

1726-1764
FROM CRADLE TO FARM

1749 *Becomes a Doctor*

JAMES HUTTON was born in Edinburgh on the third of June, 1726. His father was a highly respected merchant in the Scottish capital, where for some years he served as City Treasurer. He died, however, while James was still very young, thus leaving to his widow the responsibility of the boy's upbringing. She decided to give her son a liberal education, sending him first to the famous Edinburgh High School and then to the University, where he entered in November, 1740, as a student of humanity.

Here, quite by accident, the Professor of Logic, Stephenson, aroused in the youthful Hutton a lifelong interest in chemistry. The Professor's object was merely to illustrate by analogy some non-chemical topic upon which he was lecturing: *aqua regia,* he pointed out, can disolve gold through the joint attack of its two component acids; whereas these latter, acting separately, can only bring the baser metals into solution. This chance introduction to the science of chemistry fired Hutton's imagination, and sent him on a long search for books containing further information. All he could find at the time was a *Lexicon Technicum,* which provided an imperfect account of a few chemical subjects. Current chemistry was wholly under the sway of the phlogiston theory—Georg Ernst Stahl, coiner of the word phlogiston, had died as recently as 1734; while Anton Laurent Lavoisier, who demolished the theory, was not born till 1743. Hutton naturally, considering his date, became a phlogistonist; though towards the end a phlogistonist of very acceptable type, far removed from the original.

Hutton's lasting attachment to chemistry exercised henceforward a powerful influence upon his life. As explained in the sequel: it freed him from the clutches of the law; provided him with a comfortable income; reacted continually with his geological hypotheses; and served as cement to a particularly warm friendship with Joseph Black (1728–1799), who from 1766 held the post of Professor of Chemistry at Edinburgh after being Lecturer at Glasgow.

Black, having armed himself with a balance, was essentially a forerunner of Lavoisier, whose theory of combustion he adopted soon after its announcement in 1775; and it is pleasant to recall that Lavoisier, in sending him a copy of his combustion paper, wrote: 'all of us here consider ourselves as your disciples.' Black also made the first measurements of latent heat of fusion and evaporation, phenomena which deeply impressed Hutton's imagination. Black's further discovery, that pressure influences the course of such chemical reactions as are dependent upon the escape of a volatile, appealed to Hutton even more strongly, and led him into many speculations as to what happens in the depths of the earth, some right, some mistaken.

To return to Hutton's boyhood. In 1743 he was apprenticed to a lawyer, George Chalmers, Writer to the Sygnet. During office hours, however, he was, according to Playfair, 'often found amusing himself and his fellow apprentices with chemical experiments'; and so his master, 'with much good sense and kindness relieved him of his obligations'.

This meant a fresh start for Hutton, who now resolved to study medicine as the available subject most akin to chemistry. He began under Dr. George Young—presumably as an extramural student, for we are told that at the same time, 1744–1747, he attended classes at the University—of what he did during the '45 occupation of the capital by Bonnie Prince Charlie we have no word.

Edinburgh did not as yet give a complete course in medicine leading to a degree. Hutton, therefore, at the end of 1747 repaired to Paris, where he enthusiastically studied chemistry and anatomy (this was about 20 years before the birth of Georges Cuvier, founder of comparative anatomy). After two enjoyable years spent in this fashion, he returned by the Low Countries, taking his M.D. at Leyden, 1749, at the age of 23. His thesis was entitled *De Sanguine et Circulatione in Microcosmo.*

1750 *Turns to Agriculture*

Back in London, about the end of 1749, Hutton was worried regarding the difficulties that beset a young physician starting a practice. Probably too, as Playfair points out, he foresaw that a career of medicine would spare little time for chemical and other scientific pursuits.

Anyhow, Hutton wrote to various friends communicating his anxieties. Among his correspondents was a young man called James Davie, with whom he had formed a lasting friendship based on the fondness they shared for chemical experimentation. Before Hutton departed for the Continent, the two had started a joint investigation of the nature and production of sal ammoniac. This had already yielded some valuable discoveries, and was continued by Davie during Hutton's absence; so much so, that Davie was able to tell his friend, still in London, that there seemed a reasonable chance of profitable extraction of sal ammoniac from the soot of Auld Reekie—a popular name given to the Scottish capital because of the clouds of smoke that often hang about its chimneys. The matter has recently been inquired into by A. and N. L. Clow (*Nature,* clix, 1947, p. 425), and it appears that about this time Hutton began to receive money from the manufacture, though his name was not associated with Davie's in the title of the firm until 1765.

Relieved of pecuniary considerations, Hutton returned to Edinburgh in the summer of 1750, and decided to abandon medicine for agriculture. One reason for his choice of the latter was the charm he felt in the simplicity of a book written by an 'ingenious Mr. Tull'. The next step was a friendship struck up with Dr Manning, a Norfolk gentleman resident in Edinburgh. From him Hutton learnt of the excellence of farming practice in East Anglia, which led him in 1752 to visit Manning's father at Yarmouth. Thence he moved to Norwich, where, for more than a year under the guidance of John Dibol (Dybold), he greatly enjoyed the company of 'the most intelligent farmers' of the county. He entered into country life with much gusto, and in after years constantly spoke to his friends of the 'rural sports and little adventures' which had diverted him.

Then, having seen the method of dealing with a light soil, he passed on to High Suffolk to learn the corresponding practice on stiff clay. Here, he tells us, he found 'ploughmanship in the greatest state of perfection, more, I believe, than in any other part of the world.' He also studied dairy farming, including the making of butter.

Excursions in England lead to Geology

While in Norfolk Hutton made many journeys on foot into different parts of England, and it was during this time that he first began to take an interest in geology. Writing to Sir John Hall from Yarmouth, in 1753, he said that he was becoming very fond of studying the surface of the earth, and was looking with anxious curiosity into every pit or ditch or bed of a river which he met in his travels. Sir John Hall, Bart., was a landlord with a strong taste for science, who lived on his estate of Dunglass on the East Lothian coast bordering Berwickshire. We shall meet him again, and also make acquaintance with his son James Hall in subsequent pages.

The observations that Hutton made at this time led him to independent discovery of several fundamental facts. Thus he recognised that many solid rocks had collected as soft deposits of sand, mud, etc., in water; and that they often contain marine shells, even where they occur far inland and well above sea level; also that pebbles, frequently found in them, have in some cases been clearly derived from the breaking up of earlier consolidated sediments.

There was little in these discoveries that had not been appreciated by a few philosophers spread out over a lengthy past. Karl von Zittel, for instance, in his wonderful *History of Geology* has pointed out that some of the Greek intellectuals, as far back as Xenophanes of Colophon (born 614 B.C.), had realised that many fossil shells are remains of marine organisms; and had deduced from their distribution that continents had on occasion been invaded by the sea.

The Roman historian and traveller, Strabo, born about 63 B.C., had agreed with these views; and in addition had claimed connexion between earth-movement and volcanic activity, regarding volcanoes as safety-valves, more or less successful. Strabo's critical acquaintance with volcanoes is vouched for by his recognition of Vesuvius as a dormant example, though in his day no record existed of an eruption on its site.

Strabo, of course, was not the first to take an interest in Mediterranean volcanoes. Long previously Empedocles of Agrigentum (492–434 B.C.) had deduced from his observations at Etna that the interior of the earth must be molten. According to tradition, he paid for his curiosity by falling into the crater.

Rome too can claim an early martyr among volcanologists. Admiral Pliny (A.D. 23–79; author of *Historia Naturalis* in 30 books containing a little geology) was in command of a fleet based on

Misenum, west of Naples, when on the 24th August, A.D. 79, he saw Vesuvius blow up—thus vindicating Strabo's diagnosis. The admiral was, of course, looking at the outburst that buried Herculaneum and Pompeii. Afloat at the time, he made for Castellamara on the south shore of the Bay of Naples, where he took shelter in the house of a friend. Here to reassure those present he dined, as his son afterwards wrote to Tacitus, 'cheerfully, or what was equally splendid, with a pretence of cheerfulness', and then retired to rest. In the middle of the night, with stones falling and the house rocking, he was roused by his companions, and they decided to go into the open with protective pillows tied over their heads. The sea was too rough to face; and, though the others were able to reach safety, the poor Admiral collapsed, overcome, it seems, by noxious fumes. On the 26th of August, when the darkness of the eruption passed away and daylight returned, he was found lying where he had fallen, looking asleep rather than dead.

Exactly when Hutton came to connect consolidation and elevation of sediments with internal heat of the earth we do not know. He tells us, however, that he was not influenced in this matter by what he heard about active volcanoes, but rather by what he saw in the rocks of Britain. In his day it could not be safely assumed that volcanoes are trustworthy guides to central heat in our globe, for some regarded them as a result of near-surface combustion of coal or sulphur. Hutton himself often speaks of fire in such connexions, but here his language must be treated as metaphorical. Playfair follows suit, and we find in his *Illustrations* an apologetic explanation such as: 'fire, or more properly heat', requiring 'no circulation of air, and no supply of combustible material to support it.' (See also pp. 41, 66, 68.)

Admittedly Hutton's approach to the subject was in large measure based upon faulty argument; but, more perhaps by luck than good guidance, it led him to certain highly important conclusions that allowed of independent verification.

Another point is worth noting before we return to a consideration of past opinion concerning fossils. We all know today that carefully conducted measurements in mines show a well-nigh universal increase of temperature with depth below a superficial zone affected by seasonal fluctuations. A temperature gradient had been roughly established by Gensanne at Giromagny in the Vosges as early as 1740; but Hutton does not seem to have been aware of this discovery.

When he started his investigations he was almost completely isolated.

Now back to fossils. During the Middle Ages geology fared badly. We have seen that Greeks and Romans had recognised fossils as the shells or skeletons of once living creatures; but their successors, the schoolmen of the monasteries, explained them as some queer type of concretion. This idea continued to be held by many even after the Rennaissance, until in fact the middle of the eighteenth century. Perhaps its most distinguished adherent was the great mineralogist, George Bauer (1494–1555), better known as Agricola. On the other hand the multiple genius Leonardo da Vinci was completely modern in his appreciation of fossils and of the rocks that contain them.

English representatives among the protagonists include: Martin Lister (1638–1711) and Edward Lhuyd (1660–1709), on the side of the concretionary theory; and Robert Hooke (1635–1703), John Ray (1628–1705) and John Woodward (1665–1722), supporting the organic interpretation. It is interesting that, despite their contrasted outlook, both Lister and Hooke noticed that different beds contain different fossils. Hooke thought that this might mean a succession of faunas; but he hesitated to suggest that ammonites, for instance, have become extinct—they might still be living in the uncharted depths of the present-day oceans.

1754 *Continental Trip*

Early in the spring of 1754 Hutton set out from Suffolk to visit Flanders, where good husbandry had longest been practised. His trip took him through Holland, the Belgian provinces of Brabant and Flanders (capitals Brussels and Bruges) and French Picardy (chief town Amiens) before midsummer, when he returned to England. He was delighted with the excellent horticulture practised in Holland and Flanders; but he still retained his high regard for Norfolk agriculture. Writing from London to Sir John Hall he was able to say: 'Had I doubted it before I set out, I should have returned fully convinced that they are good husbandmen in Norfolk'.

This trip to the Continent furnished Hutton with several geological observations, some of which he later embodied in his *Theory of the Earth*.

1754-1768 *Berwickshire Farm, with Highland Excursion* 1764

At the end of the summer of 1754 Hutton returned to Scotland, and with due deliberation settled on a Berwickshire farm, called Sligh Houses, between Grantshouse and Duns. The farm-house still stands. It is quite small, and like a dozen others that are dispersed through the neighbouring countryside. It had two special attractions for Hutton: it already belonged to him as an inheritance from his father; and it brought him within 9 miles of Sir John Hall of Dunglass, whose interest in science was combined with sound sense in the conduct of country affairs.

Hutton personally brought a two-horse plough from High Suffolk, but he soon found, to use his own words, 'that it was not enough to have brought the instruments; it was equally necessary to bring the workmen in order to use them to the best advantage.' Accordingly, having 'first inclosed, drained and improved' his property, he wrote to his friends in Norfolk asking them to send a ploughman. They replied that they had been unable to persuade anyone to accept banishment in Scotland; and that the only hope was for Hutton to come and try for himself. This done, Hutton was able to pack into his post-chaise an unemployed ploughman together with another plough for the journey back to Sligh Houses. The arrival caused great amusement; but the sequel was not altogether satisfactory, for the man 'was not willing or was not fit' to train or manage others, or alternatively to work under somebody else. Hutton put up with this inconvenience for several years, but in the end it proved one of the causes of his abandoning farming.

While working keenly at his agricultural pursuits, Hutton never ceased to geologise. In 1764 he extended his experience by a trip to the north of Scotland in company with another of his numerous friends, Commissioner of Customs, afterwards Sir George Clerk. They set out by Crieff, Dalwhinnie, Fort Augustus and Inverness; then by Easter Ross to Caithness; and returned along the coast by Aberdeen to Edinburgh. It gave Hutton a first contact with crystalline schists and granites in the field.

This mention of George Clerk (1715–1784) introduces us to a remarkable family who played an important part in Hutton's scientific life. They held extensive coal properties near Edinburgh, and took keen interest in mineralogy and natural history, which, along with skill in sketching, made them particularly welcome companions on various important excursions. 'George's mind', we are told by a nephew John, 'had likewise a bent to the army, which, however, was never gratified by action, except for a few months during a rebellion in 1745.' He had many activities and was appointed a Commissioner of forfeited estates (an outcome of the '45), and Commissioner of Customs, Scotland, 1763. We shall tell on p. 58 of a curious connexion between himself and the Duke of Atholl. Meanwhile we shall find him in 1783 a founder member of the Royal Society of Edinburgh, and one of the four Presidents of its Physical Section. This is highly reminiscent of the appointment of his father, Sir John, as joint Vice-President of the Philosophical Society merged later into the Royal. George's younger brother, John Clerk of Eldin (1728–1812), seems to have been Hutton's closest associate. He was father of the John (1757–1832) who wrote the obituary of George Clerk (or Clerk-Maxwell), from which we have freely abstracted for this note.

As time went on Hutton brought his farm to such good working order that he lost some of his interest in its administration, especially as he could not devolve a share of the management on to his ploughman. Accordingly he decided to let it—he had a good offer—and to migrate to Edinburgh where he could devote himself with additional ardour to more scientific pursuits, in close touch with a brilliant group of intellectuals, already his friends.

There is a little uncertainty as to when Hutton actually severed his connexion with Sligh Houses. Playfair says on one page that he continued to live there for the most part, with occasional visits to Edinburgh, until 1768; whereas on the next he dates the removal at about 1765, the year that Hutton formally joined Davie in the sal ammoniac business. Quite possibly the 'flitting' was spread over two or three years. We shall notice presently (p. 22) four letters to an English geologist, John Strange, written about 1770, in one of which Hutton refers to the 'inconvenience of having no house, but where I am obliged to make one chamber serve me for laboratory, library and repository for self and minerals . . . the truth is that build I must or be separated from my studies'. Hutton in 1768, it may be noticed, was forty-two years old.

Though now ceasing to be a practising farmer, Hutton remained to the end very much a farmer at heart. I have always thought when reading his geological publications, that *he wrote of the earth as of a well-managed agricultural estate with a rotation designed to maintain continuing fertility*. During his last illness he nearly completed for publication a book entitled *Principles of Agriculture*. The resultant two M.S. volumes lay for long in the custody of the Geological Society of Edinburgh, to whom they were presented by James Melvin, 17 November 1887; but in 1947 they passed into the possession of the Royal Society of the same city. The occasion was a special meeting summoned to mark the hundred and fiftieth anniversary of Hutton's death. Having been asked to contribute, I thought it would be well to read this unpublished material; and I much enjoyed the experience. Though a good deal of it belongs to a later period in Hutton's life than we have reached in our narrative, it seems appropriate at this juncture to turn aside and give some indication of its contents. Passages inserted between quotes in Chapter 2 are taken verbatim from the original. I propose to confine myself to a few disconnected extracts picked out as samples.

Chapter 2

HUTTON'S PRINCIPLES OF AGRICULTURE

Inspiration

'THE OBJECT of this work', explains Hutton, 'is in short to make philosophers of husbandmen and husbandmen of philosophers. . . . I do not want to write in expectation of my book being popular, I write for my pleasure of what has been in a manner the study of my life.

'The constitution of this world has been designed by a wisdom infinitely superior to that of man, yet man in his proper wisdom aquires a certain controlling power. . . . In this world the science of man is intended to cooperate with the means employed by nature'.

Here, we must admit, a difficulty presents itself. The last two sentences quoted run counter to Hutton's basic philosophy. He held, as we shall see, that the design of nature was perfect, and that perfection cannot be improved.

Soil

Soil may be formed by 'moulder and decay' of solid rocks or less indurated bodies either 'immediately upon the place which thus had given it birth or remotely upon some other place, where it might be transported by the water or the wind'. Modern text-books still often divide soils into sedentary and transported, using these terms with reference to the materials from which the soils themselves have been derived.

The travel of material from different districts 'has long', Hutton says, 'been my particular study'. He is satisfied that in the Lowlands of Scotland a beneficial admixture is to be ascribed to marine currents during a comparatively recent submersion; and in upland districts, to floods spreading over the land. Hutton does not seem to have thought seriously of glaciation in Britain, though he was the first scientist to suggest a former great extension of glaciers in Switzerland.

Soils, he goes on to say, function as a means of support for plants, and as a source of substance. 'There are three distinct principles upon which a soil may possess its fertility. First the simple structure or mechanical construction of its mineral substance; secondly the chymical quality of its mineral substance; and lastly, the vegetable and animal substances which enter into the composition of a soil'.

Most soils consist of a mixture of sand and clay. Loam Hutton considered to be a happy blend, retentive of water owing to 'attraction of capillaries', and easily pervious to the roots of plants. Such a soil affords 'proper rooting and supply of water. . . . This is the first species of fertility. It is an inherent species; for nothing can destroy this quality'.

Air Hutton recognised, as well as water, was required by roots in a soil.

A good 'subsoil', while draining superfluous water also furnishes a reserve of moisture and of rooting space. It is interesting to find Hutton using the word 'subsoil', though in the sense of that which underlies soil, rather than of that which is partially altered into soil.

Now let us turn to an example of the second species of fertility.

'Calcareous earth with regard to vegetation, is considered by some reasoning men as being only an exciting substance, and not one that properly fertilizes; that is to say, by means of calcareous earth the soil is excited to give out its proper fertility to plants, a fertility it might otherwise withhold'—these theorists consider, in fact, that calcareous earth acts only indirectly through modifying vegetable and animal manure.

Hutton recognises profitable combined-action of calcareous earth and manure; but he deplores failure to admit the former as a fertilizer in its own right. 'Calcareous earth is a chymical principle in animal and vegetable bodies. If therefore plants are not supplied with calcareous earth from the atmosphere and rain water with which they are fed, they must receive it from the soil. But there is no reason to suppose calcareous earth is supplied to growing plants from the atmosphere or water; therefore we are constrained to look for the origin of this chymical element of vegetable bodies from the soil in which the plant had grown'.

Hutton says much more, as is his wont, but half way through he apologises. 'It had been unnecessary to engage so deeply in a question of physical principles were not an erroneous theory of this kind apt to mislead the practice of agriculture with regard to part of the art which is of the highest utility. For tho' in such cases as those in which the husbandman suspects that animal and vegetable substances are contained in the soil, he might be disposed to employ calcareous earth as a septic for those putrescible substances, yet in other cases, where he may not suspect the presence of matter proper to be affected by the septic, he would be inclined to save the labour and supersede the application of calcareous earth. This I think would be a pernicious effect of theory; and it would be much safer for the husbandman to try the effect of calcareous earth on every occasion by making the experiment, without reasoning any farther on the subject'.

Later in his manuscript Hutton gives a delightful account of a striking involuntary experiment in which he himself was involved. The marl pit, referred to below, is situated close to Sligh Houses, and its contents are of Upper Old Bed Sandstone age.

'When I first discovered marl in my ground, and opened a pit for the manuring of the fields, I did not attend to the differences of the red argillaceo-micaceous strata, some containing calcareous strata and others none, tho' all in appearance similar. The marl was dug and carted without any respect to what was good or not; and in the field, it was laid down by cartfuls. In this manner, tho' the ground was all equally and abundantly marled, spots were marled with that which contained no calcareous earth. When the corn came up, I did not perceive the effect of this when in the field, but happening to look down from the hill of Bunkle edge upon the field, from which I was then at a great distance, I saw the field in some places checkered with the deepest and palest green. I immediately went into the field, and examined the marl in those spots; and then examined the strata in the marl pit; this put the matter out of doubt; and here was an example of a small quantity of mild calcareous earth (terra calcarea aerata) in the soil, all other circumstances being the same, producing so great an effect in the operation of light or the transmutation of the sap, and making a luxuriant crop from soil which otherwise gave the most scanty.'

As regards the third type of fertility mentioned above, we read: 'All soluble animal substances become alimentary to plants, and thus produce the highest degree of fertility to vegetation'; and, farther on, 'vegetable earth may be found with a fertile or infertile soil for vegetation according as the vegetable matter is in a more soluble state on the one hand or in a more insoluble or bituminous state on the other'.

Hutton treats at length the physiology of plant life in, as might be expected, somewhat muddled fashion. The general trend of his discussion may be gathered from the following statements which I have numbered (1), (2), (3). (1) 'Every vegetable substance may be considered as properly inflamable in some degree'. (2) 'This philogistic or inflamable matter is truly formed in the process of vegetation'. (3) 'This nutritive substance by which plants receive their increase is composed in their leaves exposed to the influence of light for these leaves aquire their green colour and specific qualities only by means of being exposed to the light of day'.

The main trouble is that Hutton here makes no mention of the decomposition of atmospheric carbon dioxide by plants during their synthesis of vegetable combustible substance. The omission seems accidental for when he speaks of the reverse process, in which plant substance is destroyed, he says: 'The combustible substance, again is composed of the philogistic principle combined with the carbonic element which in being oxigenated with vital air, forms the carbonic acid, as it is now called, or fixed air, which was the name given it by Dr Black who discovered this substance, that acts so great a part in the constitution of vegetable, animal and mineral bodies.

'When this combustible substance is consumed in burning, the solar substance appears in light; and the carbonic principle is then combined with the vital air by which the body is made to burn, and thus is formed that fixed air or carbonic acid gass'.

Hutton provides a rough verbal sketch of the distribution of soil types in Great Britain. Unlike his great successor, William Smith, he scarcely ever expressed his knowledge in map form.

Climate

The uniformity of nature which Hutton's philosophy envisaged was dynamic rather than static. It was maintained by multiple cyclic operations: thus the reiterated succession of seasons is based upon astronomical causes, among which gravity counterbalances momentum; and similarly the sharing of water between oceans and continents involves evaporation followed by condensation, and air transport followed by river transport, again with gravity as an essential associate. This idea of continuing give and take supplied Hutton with constant delight and inspiration.

The astronomical causes controlling earth climates lead to local extremes of heat and cold. 'Science opens the mind of man' to the beneficence existent in the distribution of climatic zones. The extremes 'are in the wisdom of the system'. They meet the needs of special species of plants and animals.

In one feature, in particular, Hutton differed from the common run of farmers. Supported by his philosophy, he was a cheerful optimist. To grumblers who pointed to rotten hay one season, and to withered corn the next, he replied: 'Consider the reindeer and the camel—they require extremes of climate.' This answer was typical of the man, though, I admit, totally unconvincing.

Hutton attempted to establish statistical relations between temperature and crop yield, and also connexions between temperature, altitude and latitude. We receive a charming impression from his account of how, in cloudy weather, he often climbed Arthur's Seat, thermometer in hand, and always found, in wind or calm, a temperature difference of 3½°F. between his house and the summit—corresponding with a fall of 1°F. per 200 ft. of elevation; and again, from his story of how he followed 500 miles of coastline to take the temperatures of perennial springs—thus deciding that there was a drop of 1°F. in the mean annual temperature for every 2° increase of latitude.

Heredity, Beneficial or Otherwise

The following quotation illustrates how a beneficial character in one district may prove a disadvantage in another.

'In conversing with a very intelligent brewer in this City [of Edinburgh], I found he had a kind of barley from Norfolk which he commended much, altho' he had barley of a larger size from East Lothian; but this Norfolk barley was a beautiful grain and malted very kindly. I begged to have a boll of that barley, which I then sent to my farm in Berwickshire. I there multiplied it, and it prospered well. The farmers in the neighbourhood admired this grain; and some of them wished to grow it. Accordingly they sowed it, and it grew to their wish. But they soon found that, for their use, it had a material defect, or vice; this was in being tender to the wind, in its green state, and shaky after it was ripe, that is the grain coming easily from the ear. I was afterwards telling this in Norfolk to my friends, who laughed at my considering that as a fault, in this corn, which they esteemed an advantage, in being more easily threshed. But that which is a virtue for the sheltered lands of England, may be a serious vice in corn for the open fields of Scotland situated in such a windy region'.

Pure-line Selection

We may now pass on to development of new races by the selection of pure lines. When first I came upon Hutton's remarks on the subject I wondered if he had discussed the matter with Patrick Shirreff, so well known for his improvement of wheat and oats in East Lothian; but Shirreff, of course, was not born till 1792 (a capital account of Shirreff and his times is given by W. G. Smith in *Trans. Highland and Agricultural Society, Scot.,* 1910). The first two of Hutton's paragraphs, quoted below, concern China, a country that exercised a particular fascination for him, especially in regard to its non-alphabetical system of writing.

'The following story, independent of its pertinence to the subject in hand, is worth repeating; it is taken from the grand Collection upon Agriculture printed in the Palace, 1743.

' "I was walking along", says the Emperor Hang-hi, "the first days of the sixth moon, in the fields where they had sown rice, which ought not to have been reaped until the ninth; I remarked by chance a stalk of rice which was already in ear, stood above all the rest, and was sufficiently ripe to be gathered. I made it to be brought to me. The grain of it was very beautiful and well filled. This made me think of preserving it for an assay and to see if it would preserve its earliness the next year. It did preserve it in effect. All the stalks that came from it came into ear before the ordinary time and were gathered at the sixth moon. Every year, since, has multiplied the produce of the preceding harvest; and, these thirty years, it is the rice which has been served upon my table. The grain is long and the colour a little red; but it has a very good flavour and is of an agreeable taste. It is called the *Imperial Rice,* yu-mi, because it was in my garden that it began to be cultivated. It is the only rice that can be ripened to the north of the Granit Wall, where the frosts finish late and begin early; but in the Provinces to the south, where the climate is more gentle and the earth more fertile, they may easily have two crops of it in a year, and this is a pleasant consolation for me to have procured this advantage for my dear husbandmen." ' 'This beautiful story', Hutton remarks, 'should incite those who have the opportunity, of examining their fields when the ear of corn or blossoms of peas, etc., appear, and to make similar experiments, where anything occurs'.

Natural Selection

Hutton's outlook on animal breeding is equally illuminating. I had often wondered how his uniformitarian attitude would have reacted to Charles Darwin's theory of Natural Selection. To my amazement I found in his manuscript a discussion of this very subject, though admittedly limited to the diversification rather than the actual origin of species. He is dealing with domestic animals with their 'species', including various 'races', and these latter with their particular 'varieties'. How did the 'varieties' within the 'species' originate? To answer this question Hutton focuses attention upon the dog, with its strikingly different 'varieties', such as greyhound and spaniel. He sees two alternatives: (1) 'Original models' of the varieties may have 'been created with the species'. These by promiscuous breeding may have given rise to a mongrel which later may have been separated into its original constituents, 'either by continual propagation under proper circumstances in nature or by the intelligent art of man, who makes a proper selection in the breeding of those animals.' Or (2) 'On the other hand, let us suppose only one form originally in a species; and that there had been established in the constitution of the animal, a general law or rule of seminal variation, by which the form of the animal should constantly be changing, more or less, by the influence of different circumstances or in different situations; and we should in this see a beautiful contrivance for preserving the perfection of the animal form, in the variety of the species. The form of the animal would thus always be adapting itself to the instinctive arts with which the species had been induced [? endowed]; and the economy of this animal would always appear to be in perfect wisdom.

'To see this beautiful system of animal life (which is also applicable to vegetables) we are to consider, that in the infinite variation of the breed that form best adapted to the exercise of the instinctive arts, by which the species is to live, will most certainly be continued in the propagation of this animal, and will be always tending more and more to perfect itself by the natural variation which is continually taking place. Thus, for example where dogs are to live by the swiftness of their feet and the sharpness of their sight, the form best adapted to that end will be the most certain of remaining, while those forms that are less adapted to this manner of chase will be the first to perish; and, the same will hold with regard to all the other forms and faculties of the species, by which the instinctive arts of procuring its means of substance may be pursued.'

The above is remarkable as the product of a man who died twelve years before Charles Darwin was born. It bears much greater resemblance to Charles Darwin's ideas than to those of grandfather Erasmas Darwin, who was a friend of Hutton's but favoured evolutionary speculations more akin to those of Lamark.

Here let me interpolate. Through the kindness of the Royal College of Surgeons, England, I have consulted a long letter written by Hutton to Erasmus Darwin. It has been mentioned by Victor A. Eyles, who dates it approximately at 1770. It does not deal with evolution, but shows that Erasmus sometimes got his friend to place his books with Edinburgh booksellers, and that in his opinion these latter were apt to pocket all the profit. Hutton's reply is: 'Why should a philosopher make himself angry' on this account, especially a philosopher who has plenty of money already? 'For why the devil should a man have money to be a plague to him, when it is so easy to throw it away?' Most of the letter is a fanciful discussion of physics and metaphysics, partly based on a 'noble' pyrometric invention by Josiah Wedgwood. 'I see', says Hutton, 'we shall soon have science perfected in the knowledge of absolute heat and cold. . . . Let a ball of mercury be by cold contracted into nothing, . . . this will be absolute cold. . . . Let a ball of clay be by heat contracted into nothing, this is absolute heat.' (See also p. 38–9.)

It was, of course, natural that Hutton as a farmer should have thought deeply on selection. 'Mr. Bakewell', he says, 'has opened the eyes of his country men with regard to the value of this art; and by the successful application of his genius he has benefited his country more than if he had added to this kingdom tributory provinces'. Robert Bakewell was an almost exact contemporary of Hutton, 1725–1795. He is remembered as having revolutionised

British stock-breeding, notably by his work on Leicesters, longhorns and horses.

Main Contents of Hutton's M.S. "Principles"

Hutton's unpublished *Principles* is not unduly loaded with such subjects as have been noted above, which may have been written to persuade philosophers to become husbandmen. Hutton writes with equal enthusiasm on every aspect of farming: for instance, on agricultural implements and the artistry of ploughing; on the pros and cons of horses and oxen as sources of motive power; on farm labour; on rotation of crops, with a vital interval assigned to summer fallow, followed by turnips to allow of weeding; of everything appertaining to manuring, with oft-repeated condemnation of cattle as distributors of their own contribution; on the merits of ley farming under certain conditions (one is constantly reminded of Sir George Stapledon in our own time); of the breaking in of new ground; and of the advantage of forestry as an adjunct to agriculture.

The general idea of building up and maintaining the fertility of a mixed farm appealed strongly to Hutton, as it fitted in with his favourite theme of give and take leading to continuity. He admitted that lime must in many cases be artificially introduced at intervals from outside; but it is not clear that he realized that in any farm, which sells stock and crops without purchase of manure or feeding stuffs, there must be a drain on mineral resources in other directions besides lime. At the same time he strongly combats his friend Adam Smith, the celebrated economist, who held that farmers should be free to get the utmost out of their holdings without control by landlords—because, says Hutton, this would in many cases lead to temporary soil exhaustion. He, in his optimistic fashion, whimsically defends the existence of a landlord class on quite other grounds. The nation gets more out of the land if the farmer has to win not only a living for himself, but also a rent for his landlord. It is a small matter if a landlord dissipates a fortune, but it is a national calamity if a good farmer turns to idleness.

I shall conclude this outline of Hutton's *Principles of Agriculture* by selecting a particular detail. The author regarded corn as an impoverishing crop, and peas, beans and clover as fertilizing crops—though he hazarded no guess as to the chemistry of the induced fertility. He further recognised that liming promotes the growth of clover, and that, of the two clovers, white is the more serviceable for pasture, and red for harvest. More than once he refers to a Norfolk experiment in which it had been shown that red clover, closely grazed, gave poorer results in fattening stock, and left a smaller increment of fertility in the soil, than the same crop cut twice in the season. Hutton's knowledge about clover, and many other matters, was not based on personal discovery, but it exemplifies his grasp of the subject.

Chapter 3

1768-1785
EDINBURGH

ON HIS return to Edinburgh, Hutton found himself, according to Playfair, 'in the most enviable situation in which a man of science can be placed. He was in the midst of a literary society of men of the first abilities, to all of whom he was peculiarly acceptable, as bringing along with him a vast fund of information and originality, combined with that gaiety and animation which so rarely accompany the profounder attainments of science'.

The city, too, embodied the spirit of the time, for expansion had already started, which led continuously to the development of the New Town. It is symbolic that it was in 1768 that the first house of the future Princes' Street came into being. Hutton's address from some time after 1770 was in St. John's Hill at the foot of Arthur's Seat.

Hutton undoubtedly had a genius for friendship. Some friendships are lasting; Hutton's had a hereditary quality. Sir John Hall of Dunglass, who died in 1776, and John Clerk of Eldin (1728–1812), both handed on their places in Hutton's esteem to their respective sons: Sir James Hall (1761–1832), founder of experimental geology, and John Clerk, jun. (1757–1832). Sir George, brother of John, sen., has already been mentioned as having accompanied Hutton on a tour of the Highlands, 1764; and the two Johns, sen. and jun., assisted in later excursions. John, sen., according to Playfair, 'though not bred to the sea, is well known to have studied the principles of naval war with unexampled success; and though not exercising the profession of arms, he viewed every country through which he passed with the eye of a soldier as well as a geologist'. Long after his death, he was described by Robert Louis Stevenson as 'that country gentleman who, playing with pieces of cork on his own dining table, invented modern naval warfare.' There has been considerable controversy as to how far Clerk's book on naval strategy influenced the course of history, but Nelson is said to have made a careful study of its contents.

Clerk of Eldin early shared with Dr Joseph Black (1728–1799) a confidential account of Hutton's *Theory of the Earth,* and both accepted its teaching. Black's discovery of 'fixed air' (carbon dioxide) and his experiments on calcium and magnesium carbonates dated back to his doctorate thesis at Glasgow University, 1754—the year that Hutton took up residence at Sligh Houses; and his epoch-making work supplied the latter with the certainty that geological processes involving release of volatiles must be profoundly modified by subterranean pressures. To the end Black remained Hutton's dearest friend and counsellor. In many respects the natures of the two men were complementary. Playfair has summarized as follows:

'Hutton's ardour, enthusiasm, rapid thought and animation were met by Black's caution and coolness. Hutton's dread of ignorance, by Black's fear of error. Hutton's curiosity was imperious, but Black's could be laid aside. Hutton's simplicity was careless and often in collision with popular prejudice, whereas Black's was correct and respected popular prejudice'.

Adam Smith (1723–1790), famous for his *Wealth of Nations* (1776), came to live in Edinburgh in 1778. With Hutton and Black he was an original member of the Oyster Club, soon to be joined by Adam Ferguson, philosopher, Clerk of Elden, naval tactician, Robert Adam, architect, Dugald Stewart, philosopher, and John Playfair, mathematician and physicist. The three originals possessed great talents without formality; were easily amused and equally ready to speak or listen; and were sincere friends without a shade of jealousy. Visitors, artistic or scientific, from home or abroad, added to the variety of the club's meetings.

Playfair (1748–1819) is mentioned last in the above list. He was a junior member; but, as readers must by now be abundantly aware, it is due to him, more than to anyone else, that Hutton's reputation has survived. Playfair first met his hero about 1781.

Let us now turn to a particular side of the subject. Hutton in the first edition of his *Theory of the Earth,* 1785, makes scant reference to the writings of other workers. This might give the impression that he was ungenerous; but it was probably largely due to ignorance of what others had written up to date. In contrast, the book edition of his *Theory*, 1795, is flooded with quotations, mostly introduced as a source of observations to which he supplied Huttonian explanations.

Playfair puts it that he read accounts of journeys and travels in search of facts rather than theories. He adds, however, that Hutton took a delight in other people's achievements in a wide and varied field, such as Watt's improvement of the steam engine, or Cook's discoveries in the South Seas. 'The fire of his expression, on such occasions, and the animation of his countenance and manner are not to be described; they were always seen with great delight by those who could enter into his sentiments, and often with great astonishment by those who could not.'

It so happens that Hutton's generosity is capitally illustrated in four long letters already referred to on p. 8, which have recently been published with comments in the *Annals of Science,* 1951, by Mr. and Mrs. V. A. Eyles. They were addressed to John Strange, F.R.S. (1732–1799), a distinguished diplomatist, naturalist and antiquarian, regarding whom Sir Gavin de Beer has supplied interesting information in *Notes and Records of the Royal Society,* also 1951. Strange had asked Thomas Pennant, after the latter's well-known tour of Scotland, for help in regard to fossils of the country. Pennant in reply had explained that he knew too little about the subject to be of any real service, but he would like to introduce him for correspondence to Dr Hutton 'whose sole collection consists of *strata* stone; and who is the greatest enthusiast I have ever met in your way: very lively and ingenious'. Hutton's ensuing letters to Strange are full of valuable wide-spread information, admirably covered in the Eyles paper.

In regard to exchanges which Strange suggests, we read: 'There', says Hutton, 'is our Warehouse—look about you; please your own fancy; I shall hand you down any piece of stuff you desire'. He had already packed up 'some specimens . . . set apart about a year ago for your use, without the smallest expectation of return.' He had also written to his friends up and down the country to help in the good work.

In 1771 Strange went abroad, and from 1773 to 1788 was British Resident in Venice. This clearly did not sever his interest in the fossils of his own country, for we find Geikie quoting him from *Archaeologia,* 1782, as saying that 'the *Gryphites* oyster is not only found abundantly in the lower part of Monmouthshire and about Purton Passage, but also extends in considerable aggregates along the neighbouring Midland counties; having myself traced them, either in gravel or limestone, through Gloucestershire, Worcestershire, Warwickshire and Leicestershire, occupying in like manner the lowest parts of these countries, under the hills.' When Strange penned the above, 1779, William Smith, the Father of English geology based on fossils combined with superposition, was only ten years old. Strange by this time had added volcanology to his many interests, and had personally investigated the products of Italy and the Auvergne. We shall hear of him again (p. 40).

Hutton's normal time-table was fairly consistent. 'Though he rose late, he began immediately to study, and generally continued busy till dinner. He dined early, almost always at home, and passed very little time at the table; for he ate sparingly and drank no wine. After dinner he resumed his studies, or, if the weather was fine, walked for two or three hours, when he could not be said to give up study, though he might, perhaps, change the object of it. The evening he always spent in the society of his friends. No professional, and rarely any domestic arrangements interrupted this uniform course of life, so that his time was wholly divided between the pursuit of science and the conversation of his friends, unless when he travelled from home on some excursion, from which he never failed to return [except] furnished with new material for geological investigations.'

Hutton spent a good deal of his leisure in making chemical experiments. In one of these, earlier than 1772, he demonstrated the presence of alkali in a zeolite, by extracting common salt from the latter with the help of hydrochloric acid. This seems to have been the first find of alkali in a stony body. There have, of course, been many since.

1774 *Excursion, Birmingham to Cheshire and Wales*

In 1774 Hutton undertook a tour from Birmingham to Cheshire, where he visited the salt mines in company with his friend James Watt. He made observations in regard to concentric circles on the mine roof, which, unfortunately, he referred to fusion. Returning to Birmingham, he went into Wales, hoping to find a source for the 'hard gravel of granulated quartz', which he encountered so extensively in central England—this gravel must have belonged either to the Bunter Pebble Beds of the Trias, or to glacial gravels derived from the same. He found no possible source in Wales; but, turning back, he met with one at Broomesgrove, 7 miles S.W. of Birmingham, where there is a small outcrop of greatly indurated Lickey Quartzite. This satisfied him as a sample; but even so he did not find an exposed unconformable contact, which was probably the ultimate object of his exploration.

Popularity and Portraits

Hutton was fond of domestic society of both sexes, and generally sought relaxation in the evening in the house of one of his friends. 'A brighter tint of gaiety and cheerfulness spread itself over every countenance when the Doctor entered the room; and the philosopher, who had just descended from the sublimest speculations of metaphysics, or risen from the deepest researches of geology, found himself at the tea-table, as much disengaged from thought, as cheerful and gay as the youngest of the company.' He 'never married, but lived with his sisters, three excellent women', one of whom survived him.

Hutton was made the subject of several portraits. One, painted by Raeburn for one of his many friends, John Davidson of Stewartfield, is now in the possession of Lord Bruntisfield. Playfair has said that it is a good likeness: 'His figure was slender but denoted activity; while a thin countenance, a high forehead, and a nose somewhat aquiline bespoke extraordinary acuteness and vigour of mind. His eye was penetrating and keen, but full of gentleness and benignity; and his dress, plain, and all of one colour was in perfect harmony with the rest of the picture, and seemed to give a fuller relief to the characteristic features.' Robert Louis Stevenson, in reviewing some portraits by Raeburn in his *Virginibus Puerisque,* 1887, is less enthusiastic. He refers to 'Hutton the geologist, in quakerish raiment, and looking altogether trim and narrow, and as if he cared more about fossils than young ladies'.

There are also busts in the lecture hall of the Royal Society of Edinburgh, and, in London, in the Museum of the Geological Survey.

Hutton appears too in the series of *Original Portraits and Character Etchings* by John Kay (1742–1826), both alone and in company with Joseph Black. The letterpress tells us that Hutton was 'an ingenious philosopher, remarkable for the unaffected simplicity of his manner, and much esteemed by the society in which he moved'; while 'in his dress he very much resembled a quaker, with the exception that he wore a cocked hat'. Together, Hutton and Black are described as living in 'almost total ignorance of what was daily passing around them in the world.'

1777 *Coal or Culm;* 1790 *Forth-Clyde Canal*

In 1777 Hutton published his first paper, a 37-page octavo pamphlet entitled *Considerations on the Nature, Quality, and Distinctions of Coal and Culm,* a subject that must have warmed the hearts of his good friends the Clerks.

The pamphlet was intended to supply information to settle a customs dispute. In England coal paid duty, but culm, if carried coastwise, paid none. The question arose as to whether much of the small, that is disintegrated, coal of Scotland might not be rated with the culm of England. This affected some of the small coal of the Firth of Forth, which was shipped to northern counties for burning lime. The revenue officers claimed that it was duty-paying coal; the colliery owners that it should be reckoned as duty-free culm. The dispute was warm indeed, and had at last to be referred to the Privy Council. Hutton was highly successful in his investigation. He found that the coal of England was mostly 'fusible', so that small coal resulting from it tended to cake, and, thus united, to burn like big coal; whereas the culm of England is the small refuse of 'infusible' or 'stone' coal, which, failing to cake, remains, as it were, a loose sand that will not kindle in an ordinary way. On this understanding, much of the small coal of Scotland should rank as duty-free when carried coast-wise. Hutton also announced a simple criterion, which the customs officers could handle to decide whether any particular small coal should be treated as coal or culm. If a handful is thrown on to a red hot shovel and it cakes, call it coal; whereas if the pieces burn without melting down or running together, call it culm. Hutton's pamphlet helped greatly to win the day for the Forth collieries.

Hutton also took an active part in planning the course of the Forth and Clyde Canal. His writings on the subject have not been published, but the course eventually adopted was the one he had supported. The canal was opened in 1790.

1783 *Birth of the Royal Society of Edinburgh*

From his coming to live in Edinburgh, Hutton had been a member of the Philosophical Society, which had been founded about 1739 with two members of the Clerk family as Vice-Presidents. This Society published three volumes of *Essays*, 1754, 1756 and 1771. From 1777 to 1782 its meetings were fairly regular. Hutton read several papers to the Society after its last publication of *Essays* and before its incorporation in the Royal Society of Edinburgh, established, by Royal Charter, 1783. Of these only one has been published, namely: *On Certain Natural Appearances of the Ground on the Hill of Arthur's Seat*. It appeared in the second volume of *Transactions R.S.E.* Its subject was botanical, not geological.

The foundation of the Royal Society had an excellent effect upon Hutton, for it led him to publish without further delay his paper on the *Theory of the Earth*. This was read to the Society in March and April, 1785; with an *Abstract* in July, possibly the same *Abstract* as is dealt with in our next chapter. The March reading was by Black in the absence of the author due to indisposition. Publication of the paper itself, apart from the *Abstract,* awaited appearance of the first volume of the Society's *Transactions* in 1788.

Chapter 4

1785
ABSTRACT OF HUTTON'S THEORY OF THE EARTH

IT WAS long thought that 1788 was the first date at which Hutton's *Theory* reached the outer scientific world in printed form. By strange coincidence, however, in 1947, the year in which the Royal Society of Edinburgh commemorated the 150th anniversary of Hutton's death, a forgotten pamphlet came to light, entitled: *Abstract of a Dissertation read in the Royal Society of Edinburgh upon the Seventh of March, and Fourth of April, M,DCC,LXXXV, concerning the System of the Earth, its Duration and Stability.*

The occasion of the rediscovery of this *Abstract* was a sale in London of Sir James Hall's library, the same Sir James of Dunglass as had been a close friend and admirer of the living Hutton. There were two copies listed, one now in the possession of V. A. Eyles, who has been able to track down a very few others, and later, with Mrs Eyles, to prove distribution abroad in 1785.

This last achievement, recorded in *Annals of Science,* 1951, p. 337, resulted from a rereading of an article by Nicolas Desmarest, 1794 (already referred to by Archibald Geikie on p. 295 of his *Founders of Geology*). From the Eyleses we learn that Desmarest published a very slightly abbreviated interpretation of the Huttonian abstract, remarking that: 'En 1785 le Dr Hutton publia d'abord le précis de son mémoire sur la théorie de la terre, qu'il distribua à ses amis'. Geilkie makes the further point that, while Desmarest disagreed with many of Hutton's views, for instance those concerning the igneous origin of granite (published after the *Abstract*), he generously added: 'It is to Scotland that Hutton's opponents must go to amend his results and substitute for them a more rational explanation'. It was quite a habit of Desmarest to say: 'Go and see'.

The *Abstract* is reprinted in full in Eyles' contribution to the Hutton commemoration volume of the *Proceedings R.S.E.,* 1950. It is noteworthy that the title given above starting with *concerning,* is the title under which Hutton's paper was presented in 1785; and that it differs completely from the title under which this paper itself eventually appeared in 1788 (*see* Chapter 5).

The *Abstract* is about 3,000 words long, and is in almost every respect a correct and full, though highly condensed, summary of the complete paper, which is to be reviewed in detail in Chapter 5. There are, however, two significant modifications: in the first place, there is no mention of Hutton's proposition that granite has consolidated from a molten condition—presumably because someone advised against introducing so controversial an idea in regard to a matter upon which more evidence might be expected in the near future; and, in the second place, *Hutton's reiterated appeal to design in nature is reduced to three short well-balanced paragraphs, placed at the end of the article.* Here they follow a defence of Hutton's famous provocative statement that his research has revealed no 'vestige of a beginning—no prospect of an end'.

This defence runs: 'But, as there is not in human observation proper means of measuring the waste of land upon the globe, it is hence inferred, that we cannot estimate the duration of what we see at present, nor calculate the period at which it had begun;' so that, with respect to human observation, this world has neither a beginning nor an end.

The above, taken from the *Abstract,* is virtually what Playfair says later in his *Illustrations of the Huttonian Theory,* 1802, p. 119, where his object is to clear his friend of a charge of atheism: 'How often these vicissitudes of decay and renovation have been repeated [in the history of the earth] is not for us to determine: they constitute a series, of which, as the author [Hutton] of this [Uniformitarian] theory has remarked, we neither see the beginning nor the end. . . . The Author of nature has not given laws to the universe, which, like the institutions of men, carry in themselves the elements of their own destruction. He has not permitted in his works, any symptom of infancy or of old age, or any sign by which we may estimate either their future or their past duration. He may put an end, as he no doubt gave a beginning, to the present system, at some determinate period; but we may safely conclude that this great *catastrophe* will not be brought about by any of the laws now existing, and that it is not indicated by anything which we now perceive.' . . . In Hutton 'we see everywhere the utmost attention to discovery, and the utmost disposition to admire, the instances of wise and beneficent design manifested in the structure, or economy of the world. The enlarged views of these, which his geological system afforded, appeared to Dr Hutton himself as its most valuable result. They were the parts of it which he contemplated with the greatest delight; and he would have been less flattered by being told of the ingenuity of his theory, than of the addition which it had made to our knowledge of *final causes.'*

Thus Playfair clearly accepted Hutton's claim that he had detected hitherto unsuspected 'instances of wise and beneficent design in the structure or economy of the world'. All the same he refused to follow his friend in employing such instances as a foundation or support for geological theory. Actually, Playfair, in his 528-page book of *Illustrations,* 1802, develops the whole Huttonian *Theory of the Earth* with practically no other reference to design than that which we have just quoted. Hutton on the contrary, both in his 1788 paper and in his 1795 book, continually pushes the design hypothesis into the foreground. In this, he exposed himself unnecessarily, from the point of view of gaining acceptance for his geological *Theory;* but he showed great courage and honesty of purpose. Playfair was the better tactician.

The contrast is emphasised in the following two quotations: What, asks Hutton, is the final cause of the universal waste we see about us? 'Is it in order to destroy the system of this living world, that the operations of nature are thus disposed upon the surface of this earth? Or, Is it to perpetuate the progress of that system which, in other respects, appears to be contrived with so much wisdom? Here are questions which a Theory of the Earth must solve; and here, indeed, must be found the most material part by far of any Theory of the Earth'. On p. 2 of his *Illustrations,* Playfair quietly answers: 'to examine their causes, and thus to connect together all the indications of change that are found in the mineral kingdom, is the proper object of a Theory of the Earth.'

Here I must explain that I consider Hutton's approach mistaken, but not unscientific, nor yet deductive in opposition to inductive. (It was a habit of the time for any controversialist to denounce his opponents' arguments as deductive, and to praise his own as inductive.) Hutton started from observations made by himself, which, he thought, confirmed a very general assumption that certain aspects of nature had been designed for the welfare of mankind. The circulation of water from the oceans through the atmosphere and back through the rivers was a case in point. He then justifiably reasoned that there must be design in countless other cases, design which till now had often escaped recognition. Instances which greatly interested him concerned the consolidation and upheaval of marine sediments. This led him to look more deeply into nature's operations, and he found in them what he took to be additional examples. All told, however, the design hypothesis served him merely as a scaffolding. The bricks and mortar of his *Theory* were supplied by critical observations of natural processes. Playfair, though he accepted Hutton's views well nigh in their entirety, wished that his friend would, in the printed word, treat design as though it were a serial discovery, rather than a guide. The *Abstract* puts it: 'That there is nothing visionary in this theory, appears from its having been rationally deduced from natural events, from things that have already happened; things which have left in the particular constitution of bodies, proper traces of the manner of their production; and things which may be examined with all the accuracy, or reasoned upon with all the light that science can afford.'

Let us now turn to the three final paragraphs of the *Abstract*. They read:

(1) 'An endeavour is then made to support the theory by an argument of a moral nature, drawn from a consideration of a final cause. Here a comparison is formed between the present [Uniformitarian] theory, and those [Catastrophic theories] by which there is necessarily implied either evil or disorder in natural things; and an argument is formed upon a supposed widsom of nature, for the justice of a theory in which perfect order is to be perceived.

(2) 'According to the [Uniformitarian] theory, a soil, adapted to the growth of plants, is necessarily prepared, and carefully preserved; and, in the necessary waste of land which is inhabited the foundation is laid for future continents, in order to support the system of this living world.

(3) 'Thus, either in supposing Nature wise and good, an argument is formed in confirmation of the [Uniformitarian] theory, or, in supposing the theory to be just, an argument may be established for wisdom and benevolence to be perceived in nature. In this manner, there is opened up to our view a subject interesting to man who thinks; a subject on which to reason with relation to the system of nature; and one which may afford the human mind both information and entertainment'.

Put more briefly, the first of these three paragraphs states that Hutton's paper (though not the earlier part of its *Abstract*) has endeavoured to find support for the Uniformitarian theory by linking it with the prevalent hypothesis of divine design in nature.

The second merely picks out two sample features of the theory to which Hutton has given a design interpretation.

The third points out that such support as is mentioned in the first paragraph must be mutual. It also seems to imply that the Uniformitarian theory, unaided, may be fruitfully employed as a basis for further investigation of nature.

All this raises the question of the authorship of the *Abstract*. Eyles has argued, according to evidence that at first sight seems conclusive, that Hutton himself prepared it. He undoubtedly agreed to its distribution; but, in my opinion, he could not and would not have written it. The geology is the geology of Hutton, but the voice is the voice of Playfair.

Chapter 5

1785-1788

'THEORY OF THE EARTH; OR AN INVESTIGATION OF THE LAWS OBSERVABLE IN THE COMPOSITION, DISSOLUTION, AND RESTORATION OF LAND UPON THE GLOBE

BY JAMES HUTTON, M.D., F.R.S. EDIN. AND MEMBER OF THE ROYAL ACADEMY OF AGRICULTURE AT PARIS'

(Read R.S. Edin., 1785; published Trans. R.S. Edin., 1788)

'Part I. Prospect of the Subject to be treated of'

HUTTON STARTS with the assurance that there is design in nature. 'We perceive a fabric, erected in wisdom, to obtain a purpose worthy of the power that is apparent in the production of it'. This purpose, we are told, is to maintain the earth as 'a habitable globe', where, 'upon the surface, . . . the more inert matter is replenished with plants, and with animal and intellectual beings.' Since living creatures are part of the purpose, 'we are not to look for nature in a quiescent state; matter itself must be in motion; and the scenes of life a continued or repeated series of agitations and events'. In these, 'science may find a fit subject of investigation in every particular, of *form, quality,* or *active power,* that presents itself in this system of motion and of life'; and we 'are led to acknowledge an order, not unworthy of Divine wisdom.'

This introductory statement furnishes a good example of Hutton's reiterated reference to divine design in the development of his *Theory of the Earth;* but it also clearly sets forth the propriety of a scientist going directly to nature, as God's handiwork, there to study earth processes instead of relying upon recorded revelation. Furthermore, it must be remembered that introduction of religious concepts into scientific disquisitions was in Hutton's day quite fashionable, though not universally approved. We have seen in the previous chapter Playfair's reaction against the mixing of the two.

Hutton next points out that our globe is a machine, which, in regions accessible to observation, is made of three parts: 'a solid body of earth, an aqueous body of sea, and an elastic body of air'; while, out of sight, there is a central body supporting the three accessible parts. This central body, we are warned, is 'not solid and inert', as commonly supposed.

Hutton then briefly reviews some of the services necessary for life, which we receive from the three visible parts of our globe. His fondness for cyclic continuity finds expression in his description of the ocean, a matter to which we have already referred. The ocean, to use his own words, is 'the receptacle of the rivers, and the fountains of our vapours;' which latter are produced in co-operation with the atmosphere in 'raising up the water of the ocean, and pouring it forth upon the surface of the earth.' Similarly, he points out that the *vis inertia* of our planet is combined with gravitation. Otherwise our earth would 'be for ever removed from its end . . . as a globe sustaining plants and animals, which may be termed a living world.'

As for light and heat, without attempting to explain their laws, we are well aware of the essential benefits which they bring to us. Regarding electricity and magnetism, we admittedly are more ignorant still, not even knowing their value 'in the operation of this globe'; but 'powers of such magnitude or force are not to be supposed as useless in a machine contrived surely not without wisdom.'

Let us now follow up more closely this idea that, where relative motion is involved, some compensating tendency is required to maintain any advantage that depends upon position. 'A solid land could not have answered the purpose of a habitable world; for a soil is necessary to the growth of plants; and a soil is nothing but the material collected from the destruction of the solid land . . . and is necessarily washed away, by the continued circulation of the water, running from the summits of the mountains towards the general receptacle of that fluid. . . . Our fertile plains are formed from the ruins of our mountains. . . . The travelling materials are still pursued by the moving water', and 'delivered into the sea, cannot, for a long continuance, rest upon the shore; for, by the agitation of the winds, the tides and currents, every moveable thing is carried farther and farther along the shelving bottom of the sea, towards the unfathomable regions of the ocean.'

Unbalanced progress in the production and removal of soil would in an immensity of time destroy all land; and we should 'perceive an end to this beautiful machine'. Let us therefore inquire whether or no 'the necessary decay of the machine is naturally repaired'. Here we find Hutton's first mention in this paper of what today is often spoken of as *geological time*. Recovery might take so long as not to be clearly apparent in human history. The Mosaic record (here referred to for the first of three times) places the 'beginning of man at no great distance; and there has not been found in natural history, any documents by which a high antiquity might be attributed to the human race.'

Accordingly the question arises as to how to interpret evidence provided by very ancient rocks. The answer comes back: 'In examining things present, we have data from which to reason with regard to what has been'—hence we have what may be taken as Hutton's first statement of the doctrine later called *Uniformitarianism*. Working on this principle it is fruitful to inquire 'how the waste of a habitable globe' may be repaired.

Hutton starts on the task by giving his interpretation of 'the solid parts of our globe', the progenitors of soil. These, he says, are in general 'composed of sand, of gravel, of argillaceus and calcareous strata'; and 'appear to have been the production of water, winds, and tides.' The water, he claims, is proved by fossils to have been the water of the sea, capable of supporting the life of shell-fish and corals.

After drawing attention to problems posed by the consolidation and relative elevation of marine sediments, Hutton concentrates attention on the past nature of unfossiliferous sparry limestones. These, he decides, are sufficiently often linked through transitional types with fossiliferous limestones to warrant their interpretation as much altered examples of the same. Here Hutton introduces the idea of *metamorphism,* though the word itself was scarcely used until it was popularised by his successor Lyell.

In assembling his evidence, Hutton quotes from the celebrated Genevan geologist, Horace Benedicte de Saussure (1740–1799), who devoted his life to exploration of the Alps, with various first ascents to his credit, including that of Mont Blanc, 1787. Already the first volume of his *Voyages dans les Alpes* had been published, 1779; and three others were yet to appear, 1786, 1796, 1796. He was the author upon whom Hutton most relied for observations concerning really big mountains. The particular point which concerned Hutton at the moment was a bed standing at about 2,150 m. above the sea, which de Saussure described as 'un roc calcaire, ou marbre grossier', though containing fragments of oyster shells.

Hutton now turns aside to mention 'certain mountains and masses of granite. . . . These', he says, reserving for a later page his own interpretation, 'are thought to be still older in their formation, and are very rarely, at least, found superincumbent on strata which must be acknowledged as products of the sea.'

Having said so much, he returns to the apparently unconnected topic of the continent-wide position of marine sediments above present sea-level. He briefly argues that this cannot be ascribed to redistribution of the sea 'caused by this earth revolving in the Solar System.' No! It must be a terrestrial phenomenon resulting from differential earth-movement; and it should be investigated along with the associated phenomenon of consolidation, commonly found in sediments that now stand above the level of the sea.

Consolidation, Hutton claims, is (apart from 'stalactital and certain ferruginous concretions') 'performed at the bottom of the ocean, or under great depths of the earth, of which our continents are composed'. It lies out of reach of our immediate observations, but 'here the science of Chemistry must be brought particularly to our aid'. Although he does not say so, Hutton was thinking of Black's experiments on the retention of volatiles by bodies heated under high pressures.

Having thus whetted our appetites, Hutton withholds for the most part his explanation of consolidation for Part II; meanwhile, however, he supplies a foretaste of one aspect of the evidence which is to be developed later.

'The loose materials', he says, 'that have subsided from water', have been 'formed into masses of the most perfect solidity, having neither water nor vacuity between their various constituent parts, nor in the pores of those constituent parts themselves'.

'Part II. An Investigation of the Natural Operations Employed in Consolidation of the Strata of the Globe'

'Strata formed at the bottom of the sea, are to be considered as having been consolidated, either by aqueous solution, or by the effect of heat and fusion.'

Hutton thinks he can negative consolidation by aqueous solution. In the first place he argues that the residual water left after deposition of cement would require space for itself; and he has already told us at the end of Part I that thoroughly consolidated sediments are devoid of such space, however distributed.

Hutton goes so far as to admit the possibility of partial consolidation by precipitation of water-carried cement; still this must be on a very small scale unless the solution can be replaced by circulation—but how, he asks, can circulation be maintained on the bottom of the ocean, where, he is certain, most consolidation has occurred?

Moreover 'if water had been the menstruum by which the consolidating matter was introduced into the interstices of strata, those bodies could only be found consolidated with such substances as water is capable of dissolving'; but we find 'strata made solid by the formation of fluor, . . . sulphureous and bituminous substances, . . . feldspar, . . . and almost all the various metallic substances, with their almost endless mixtures and sulphureous compositions'. All these, 'so far as we know', are insoluble. True, 'we have strata consolidated by calcareous spar' and 'siliceous matter', but these are 'in a state totally different from that under which' they have 'been observed, on certain occasions, to be deposited by water'—as stalactite or sinter. Hutton's conclusion is:

'If again it is by heat or fusion that the loose and porous structures of strata shall be supposed to have been consolidated, then every difficulty which had occurred in reasoning upon the power or agency of water is at once removed. The loose and discontinuous body of a stratum may be closed by means of softness and compression; the porous structure of the materials may be consolidated in a similar manner, by the fusion of their substance; and foreign matter may be introduced into the open structure of strata, in the form of steam or exhalation, as well as in the fluid state of fusion; consequently heat is an agent for the consolidation of strata, which water alone is not'. It is implicit in his spatial argument that heat can pass through a solid body without aid from visible channels.

Hutton was, of course, right to the extent that heat does play some part in the consolidation of sediments—a major part in regard to hornfelses and crystalline schists; but much of his argument was mistaken, and the conclusions based upon it were in some cases quite wrong, though in others correct. Thus he misinterpreted flint as a product of complete melting. He was influenced in this by the hardness and transgressive nature of flint, and by the fact that siliceous substance seems to be insoluble in pure water, though rendered soluble by alkaline substance present in the geysers of Iceland. He also attached importance to the fact that invading flint has a sharp junction, not diffuse as one would expect it to be if it had resulted from soaking. He was much impressed by what he had seen of the behaviour of flint in the chalk of England, France and Belgium, and in fossil wood from England, Germany and Lough Neagh, Ireland. He was misled by appearances, but who with field experiences of flint can blame him for that?

Hutton next turned to the contents of mineral veins. A rather full quotation is given below as it furnishes a comment on the connexion subsisting between mineralogy and chemistry at the time of his writing.

'Here, for example, are crystallized together in one mass, *first, Pyrites,* containing sulphur, iron, copper; 2*ndly, Blende,* a composition of iron, sulphur, and calamine; 3*rdly, Galena,* consisting of lead and sulphur; 4*thly, Marmor metallicum,* being the terra ponderosa [barytes], saturated with the vitriolic acid, a substance insoluble in water; 5*thly, Fluor,* a saturation of calcareous earth, with a peculiar acid, called the acid of spar, also insoluble in water; 6*thly, Calcareous spar,* of different kinds, being calcareous earth saturated with fixed air, and something besides, which forms a variety in this substance; *lastly, Siliceous substance* or *Quartz crystals.* All these bodies, each possessing its proper shape, are mixed in a manner . . . which may be expressed in general by saying that they are mutually contained in, and contain each other'. Hutton maintains that 'it is in vain to look for the explanation of these appearances in the operations of nature, by means of aqueous solution', rather than of heat.

Hutton was certainly right in supposing that heat has helped in the production of many mineral veins; though he was wrong in refusing to heat, in this matter, the cooperation of water. Perhaps we are entitled to say that he was right enough to justify his hypothesis that many mineral veins indicate a high temperature in the earth's interior at the time of their formation.

Hutton soon passes on to the 'inflammable bodies called oily or bituminous'. Here he offers an explanation of the rank problem of coal seams, attributing rank to thermal metamorphosis, as most people do today. The following quotation makes the point clear:

'The strata of fossil coal are found in almost every intermediate state, as well as in those of bitumen and charcoal. Of the one kind [bituminous] is that fossil coal which melts or becomes fluid on receiving heat; of the other [anthracite] is that species of coal found in Wales and Scotland, which is perfectly infusible in the fire, and burns like coaks, without flame or smoak. The one species abounds in oily matter, the other has been distilled by fire, until it has become *caput mortuum,* or perfect coal.

'The more volatile parts of these bituminous bodies are found in their separate strata on some occasions.' Of this Hutton gives a particularly interesting example:

'I have in my possession the most undoubted proof of this kind. It is a mineral vein, or cavity, in which are blended together coal of the most fixed kind, quartz and marmor metallicum. Nor is this all; for the specimen now referred to is contained in a rock which every naturalist now-a-days will allow to have congealed from a fluid state of fusion'.

The rock mentioned in the last sentence is undoubtedly basalt; and it is interesting historically to find Hutton saying that its origin was already *universally* accepted before he himself had presented his *Theory* to the Royal Society of Edinburgh in 1785. He knew by this time a fair amount about the struggle that had divided Continental geologists on the subject; but he was optimistic in supposing the battle won, for it continued vigorously long after his death. In Playfair's *Illustrations,* 1802, p. 274, the Neptunian system is admitted to have 'become the prevailing system of geology'.

Passing over what he has to say about Cheshire salt, we find Hutton drawing comparisons between septarian nodules and what 'the German mineralogists have termed *Drusen*'. It is enough here to outline his interpretation of the former. The examples he describes are ironstone nodules in Carboniferous Shales at Aberlady on the Firth of Forth. Each has, according to him, an unbroken, impervious crust of ironstone, which must effectively have sealed off the interior, during its cracking stage, from exchange of matter with the outside world. The complete development of the interior, with residual patches of shrunk stone separated by calcspar-lined septa, must therefore have been due to conduction-carried heat.

From this, according to Hutton, it 'necessarily follows that the contraction of the ironstone, in order to form septa, and the filling of their cavities with spar, had proceeded *pari passu;* and that this operation must have been brought about by means of fusion, or by congelation from a state of simple fluidity and expansion'. One may be pardoned for doubting whether this is a necessary conclusion.

It may be connected with what he has said about Wedgwood's noble pyrometric invention (p. 17).

We now come to something more welcome, namely admission that a melt under pressure may occasionally hold water in solution. Agates sometimes include central water, and this he explains as follows: 'Let us only suppose a sufficient degree of compression in the body of melted glass, and we can easily imagine it to receive and confine water, as well as any other substance.' It is good to find Hutton thus recognising hydrothermal possibilities under high pressure, even if the context is not all that can be desired.

Now to consider 'strata consolidated without the introduction of foreign matter, merely by softening of their own materials'. Hutton takes, for example, one simple homogeneous body, in order to exhibit it in the various degrees of consolidation, from the state of simple incoherent earth to that of the most solid marble. It is chalk; naturally a soft calcareous earth, but which may also be found consolidated in every different degree.

'Through the middle of the isle of Wight there runs a ridge of indurated chalk. This ridge runs from the isle of Wight directly west into Dorsetshire, and goes by Corfe-castle towards Dorchester, perhaps beyond that place. The sea has broke through this ridge at the west end of the isle of Wight, where columns of the indurated chalk remain, called the Needles; the same appearance being found upon the opposite shore in Dorsetshire.

'In this field of chalk, we find every gradation of that soft earthy substance to the most consolidated body of this indurated ridge, which is not solid marble, but which has lost its chalky property, and has acquired a kind of stony hardness.

'We want only further to see this cretaceous substance in the most indurated and consolidated state; and this we have in the north of Ireland, not far from the Giants Causeway. I have examined cargoes of this limestone brought to the west of Scotland, and find the most perfect evidence of this body having been once a mass of chalk, which is now a solid marble.

'Thus, if it is by means of fusion that the strata of the earth have been, in many places, consolidated, we must conclude, that all the degrees of consolidation, which are indefinite, have been brought about by the same means'.

Hutton based his description of the Isle of Wight and Dorset on a personal visit to which he refers in one of his letters to Strange, written about 1770. It is probable that he was attracted to the district by discussions current among fellow scientists. At any rate we find the Swede Alex Frederic Cronstedt in his *Essay towards a System of Mineralogy* (1758, English editions 1770, 1772) placing 'earths and stones in one class, because 1 . . . they consist of the same principles; 2 . . . they are by turns converted from one into the other . . . Where is it that the common chalk finishes, and the limestone begins in the English strata?'

We now arrive at Hutton's famous claim, here advanced for the first time in print so far as he was concerned, that *granite* has consolidated from complete fusion. Granite, made of quartz, felspar and mica, is 'perfectly solid', like the most indurated sediment already considered; but it differs in being 'not generally stratified'.

Here we may interpolate to take note of an almost forgotten anticipation by Strange. It is contained in a letter which this wandering diplomat (p. 23) wrote to Sir John Pringle, and which was published in the *Philosophical Transactions,* 1775, as an 'Account of two Giants Causeways in the Venetian state, etc.' In it Strange made the suggestion that granite, along with much that is called basalt is igneous, though not volcanic—Hutton's position exactly. Playfair, commenting on this in his *Illustrations,* p. 265, writes: 'These opinions had not, I believe, occurred at that time to any mineralogist except Dr Hutton, nor had they been communicated by him to any but a few of his most trusted friends; for that Mr Strange has without doubt all the merit of a first discoverer. Indeed, without the knowledge of the principle of compression, such as it is laid down by Dr Hutton, it was hardly possible for him to proceed further than he has done'.

To return to Hutton: 'The nature of granite as part of the structure of the earth is too intricate a subject to be here considered, where we only seek to prove the fusion of a substance from the evident marks which are to be observed in a body. We shall therefore only now consider one particular species of granite; and if this shall appear to have been in a fluid state of fusion, we shall be allowed to extend this property to all of the kind.

'The species now to be examined comes from the north country, about four or five miles west of Portsoy, on the road to Huntly. I have not been upon the spot, but am informed that this rock is immediately connected or continuous with the common granite of the country. This indeed appears in the specimens that I have got;

for in some of these, there is to be seen a gradation from the regular to the irregular sort'.

Hutton undoubtedly made a happy choice in concentrating upon the specimens collected along the Huntly road. They show to perfection what is called graphic or pegmatitic texture. His very full account runs to two pages quarto of text with a plate of ten figures. I for one agree that 'there is sufficient evidence of this body having been consolidated by fusion, and in no other manner.'

Hutton's contemporaries, however, were slow to accept this conclusion, for it broke with a particularly strong tradition. Granite is so often covered unconformably by associated sediments that there is a tendency to take it as something essentially older, the product of a primaeval ocean with peculiar characteristics. Also, if granite had really once been molten, why did it differ so strongly in texture from present-day lavas?

One of the last things that Hutton deals with in Part II is jointing due to cooling. There is no doubt that some joints have originated in this way; but few indeed would agree that 'there is no consolidated stratum that wants these appearances.' Still, it gave him great pleasure to find, as he thought, such wide-spread corroboration of internal heat. 'Error', he says, 'never can be consistent, nor can truth fail of having support from the accurate examination of every circumstance'.

'Part III. Investigation of the Natural Operations Employed in the Production of Land above the Surface of the Sea'

Hutton claims a designed connexion between consolidation and upheaval; for, if the purpose of upheaval is to provide land above sea level, it would be of little avail to raise unconsolidated sediments, liable to rapid destruction.

He has already shown us, to his own satisfaction, that loose sediments are consolidated by heat before upheaval. This suggests that heat may be responsible for upheaval as well as consolidation. We need not explain how deep-seated heat has arisen. It is enough, at this stage, to have become aware of its existence. (See pp. 5, 66, 68).

After general argument in favour of upheaval of land rather than withdrawal of sea, Hutton points out that the strata of the globe are found in every possible attitude, horizontal, vertical, discontinuous, broken, bent and doubled. This establishes earth-movement, presumably often accompanied by uplift. He concludes that 'the land on which we dwell' has been elevated 'by extreme heat, and expanded with amazing force . . . for the purpose of the living world'.

Mineral veins are, according to Hutton, an obvious concomitant of these disturbances. They are, 'in some measure, a continuation of that mineral region, which lies necessarily out of all possible touch of our examination'.

Hutton, with some exaggeration, contrasts the fissures occupied by mineral veins with the universal jointing which he has already ascribed to cooling. 'Every species of fracture, and every degree of dislocation and contortion, may be perceived in the form of mineral veins'—whereas in ordinary jointing one only sees 'simple separation and measured contraction'. The material of the veins often stands in the same causal relationship to the rents which it occupies, as if it were a wedge of wood, iron or ice. The material of the veins also agrees with that already described as injected in molten condition interstitially with attendant brecciation.

'In order to form as well as fill those veins . . . requires an elevating power of immense force'. This some philosophers find difficult to admit, 'but when fire bursts forth from the bottom of the sea, and when the land is heaved up and down, so as to demolish cities in an instant, and split asunder rocks and solid mountains, there is nobody but must see in this a power, which may be sufficient to accomplish every view of nature in erecting land, as it is situated in the place most advantageous for that purpose . . . the production of such land as this which we inhabit.'

Hutton now turns quite naturally to a consideration of active and recently extinct volcanoes, of which he has no personal experience. At Etna, he says, a 'stream of melted lava flows' from an 'immense height, . . . and rocks of enormous size are projected from its orifice some miles into the air. . . . Every one acknowledges that here is the liquefying power and expansive force of subterranean fire, or violent heat'. The significance of this account is not much impaired by the fact that Hutton connects with it a remark that an associated Sicilian marble has 'flowed, and been in such a state of fusion as lava'. He had drawn this conclusion from examination of a marble table in his possession. I do not propose to follow up the argument which he based upon it, beyond quoting one apposite sentence: Man 'does not always reason without error'. This of course was addressed as a reproof to his opponents.

As already remarked on p. 38, Hutton, by this time knew that Continental geologists had been, at any rate previous to 1785, divided into two camps in regard to the former existence of volcanic activity in regions which today are completely quiescent: the Vulcanists, who followed two French scientists, Jean Etienne Guettard (1715–1786) and Nicolas Desmarest (1725–1815); and the Neptunists, whose leader, but not originator, was the redoubtable Abraham Gottlob Werner (1749–1817) of Freiberg in Saxony. Hutton does not mention either names or dates in this connexion; but we may add:

Guettard discovered extinct volcanoes in the Auvergne, 1752, though he regarded columnar basalt as a crystallisation product of an aqueous fluid.

Desmarest realised the volcanic origin of columnar basalt in the Auvergne, and, by analogy, in the far away cliffs of the Giant's Causeway, in 1763, read a paper on the subject in 1765, and published in 1774.

Hutton's corresponding dates are: about 1760, when he recognised the igneous origin of whin or whinstone (a local name for the old basalts of Scotland); 1785, when he made his first published announcement of the same in the *Abstract* of his *Theory of the Earth;* and 1788, when he gave a castrated account in the complete paper as published in the *Transactions R.S.Edin.*—see pp. 38 and 46.

Another British date which should perhaps be added here is 1772, when Sir Joseph Banks, the perennial President of the Royal Society of London, visited Staffa on his way to Iceland along with Dr Solander and Archbishop Troil (p. 90). Banks' descriptions, sketches and measurements were published in Thomas Pennant's *Tour in Scotland,* 1774, and soon made Staffa famous throughout Europe. Though Banks did not enter into theoretical discussions, he called the Staffa rock 'Basaltes, very much resembling the Giant's Causeway in Ireland', and he compared some of its appearances with those of lavas. Banks' account of Staffa must have been familiar to Hutton, but is never mentioned in his writings.

The main date in the history of the Neptunist opposition is 1776, when, a year after his appointment as professor at Freiberg, Werner declared against the igneous origin of a Saxon basalt responsible for the castle-crowned hill of Stolpen. He seems to have known, at the time, of Desmarest's claim of 1774, but he himself 'found not a trace of volcanic action, nor the smallest proof of volcanic origin'. All this is set out in Geikie's chapter on Werner in his *Founders of Geology*. Here also we find a reference to a confirmatory visit paid by Werner to another basalt, near Scheibenberg in the Erzgebirge. In this case we have a fuller coverage in Playfair's *Illustrations,* p. 279, where an extensive quotation is introduced in the original French from a 1791 paper by Werner, accompanied by a partial English translation. This tells of repeated gradations in a sequence of sand, under clay, under wacke, under basaltes, and of the effect which the gradations produced upon their investigator. 'I was irresistably led', said Werner, 'to conclude, that the basaltes, the wacke, the clay, and the sand, are all one and the same formation; and that they are all the effect of a chemical precipitation during one and the same submersion of this country'.

Hutton must have known of Werner's continued claim that so-called extinct volcanoes are of aqueous origin; but we have seen on p. 38 that he appears to have considered this alternative interpretation as already demolished by 1785. The following quotation conveys the same impression, when it tells us that, in examining modern lavas, 'men of science find a character of such productions, in generalizing the substance, and understanding the natural constitution of those bodies. It is in this manner that such a person, finding a piece of lava in any place of the earth, says with certainty, Here is a stone which had congealed from a melted state.

'Having thus found a distinguishing character for those fused substances called, in general, lavas, and having the most visible marks for that which had been actually a volcano, naturalists, in examining different countries, have discovered the most undoubted proofs of many ancient volcanos, which had not been before suspected. Thus volcanos will appear to be not a matter of accident, or as only happening in a particular place; they are general to the globe, so far as there is no place upon the earth that may not have an eruption of this kind; although it is by no means necessary to have had those eruptions'.

It is to be noted that Hutton, in the above, combines cone-and-crater topography, or, as he puts it, 'visible marks for that which had been actually a volcano', with the nature of the constituent rocks in diagnosing extinct volcanoes. We shall in due course find that this was one reason for his failure to see true volcanoes in Britain—only underground counterparts. For the present let us continue our quotation:

'Volcanos are natural to the globe, as general operations, but we are not to consider nature as having a burning mountain for an end in her intention, or as a principal purpose in the general system of this world. The end of nature in placing an internal fire of power of heat, in the body of this earth, is to consolidate the sediment collected at the bottom of the sea, and to form thereof a mass of permanent land above the level of the ocean, for the purpose of maintaining plants and animals. The power appointed for this purpose is, as on all other occasions, where the operation is important, and where there is any danger of a shortcoming, wisely provided in abundance; and there are contrived means for disposing of the redundancy. These, in the present case are our volcanos.

'A volcano is not made on purpose to frighten superstitious people into fits of piety and devotion, nor to overwhelm devoted cities with destruction; a volcano should be considered as a spiracle to the subterranean furnace, in order to prevent the unnecessary elevation of land, and fatal effects of earthquakes; and we may rest assured, that they, in general, wisely answer the end of their intention, without being themselves an end for which nature had exerted such amazing power and excellent contrivance'.

Hutton's picture of volcanoes as safety valves was probably taken from Strabo, who had already employed this metaphor some eighteen hundred years previously. In confirmation we find that Hutton, after mentioning high-placed volcanoes in the Andes and round the Alps in France, Germany and Italy, recalls by way of contrast 'the new island near Santorini'—this new island had erupted in 196 B.C., and had been described by Strabo. At the same time, Hutton may also have been influenced by conversations with his friend James Watt of steam engine fame.

Hutton considered that molten matter, breaking ground on land, is relatively free to pour out as lavas and ashes, and so to build genuine volcanoes with cones and craters; whereas, if the molten matter emerges on the bottom of the sea, it is likely to be checked by contact with the water. He thus accounts for great quantities of once-fused matter occurring 'among the strata of the earth, where there are no visible marks of any volcanos'.

This emphasises for Hutton the differences between 'subterraneous lavas' (we call them intrusions) and 'proper lavas': the former are actual elevators, and result from 'melted matter, analogous to lava, . . . forced to flow among the strata'; whereas the latter have issued out of a volcano.

Hutton then proceeds to classify the igneous rocks of the Vulcanists in the Auvergne, Eifel, Italy, etc., as 'proper lavas', and the whinstones of Scotland and elsewhere as 'subterraneous lavas'. He takes great pleasure in this idea, for in it 'we have discovered the secret operations of nature concocting future land, as well as those by which the present habitable earth has been produced from the bottom of the abyss'.

At this stage of his presentation, Hutton writes as though he had already explained to his readers how and why whinstone should be recognised as igneous. He had indeed argued for the igneous origin of flint and granite; but, up to date, his only reference to the igneous nature of whinstone is carried in a statement in Part II of this chapter. In this we read of certain 'nodules contained in the whinstone, porphyry, or basaltes of the Calton-hill by Edinburgh; a body which is to be afterwards examined, when it will be found to have flowed, and to have been in fusion, by the operation of subterraneous heat.'

Actually, Hutton had early, and independently, recognised the molten origin of whinstone, because: it is unfossiliferous; devoid of stratification and detrital texture; outstandingly hard; appreciably crystalline; and often transgressive, though always insoluble. Later, when he became aware of the discoveries of the Vulcanists, he recognised that his whinstones corresponded closely with their lavas. He felt that he had been anticipated, and that it was no use parading his own, as we think splendid, discovery, in so far as it was based upon the same sort of arguments as had already been used by the Vulcanists.

Why then did he make an exception in regard to the Calton Hill whin? The mere fact that it is a convenient locality does not, I think, furnish a sufficient answer. I have no doubt that Hutton here realised with pleasure that his argument was peculiar to himself—was unforestalled. Unfortunately, it was based upon a mistaken interpretation of crystalline amygdales. These, Hutton imagined to be enclosures which had passed through a molten condition. The Vulcanists, on the other hand, correctly regarded them as the infilling of vesicles.

Hutton now lists a whole series of names, which, he considers, correspond in other countries with the whin of Scotland: Trap in Norway and Sweden; ragstone in Staffordshire; Amygdaloid and Schwartzstein in Germany; toadstone in Derbyshire; and basalt in the Giant's Causeway. In making these identifications he acknowledges help from Cronstedt's *Mineralogy* (English editions 1770, 1772), already referred to on p. 40. The *Mineralogy* does not include the Scottish name whinstone; nor do we find any reference to the rocks concerned. Cronstedt was a chemical mineralogist, with his lips tightly closed on a blowpipe. His object was to classify, rather than to explain.

For Scottish whinstone or whin Hutton cites the great Midland Valley as the type area; but he uses it to emphasise differences, rather than resemblances, between 'whin' (interpreted as intrusive) and 'lava' (interpreted as extrusive).

'The strata in this region', Hutton says, 'consist, in general, of sandstone, coal, limestone or marble, and marl or argillaceous strata, with strata of analogous bodies, and various compositions of these. But what is to the present purpose is that, through all this space, there are interspersed immense quantities of whinstone; a body which is to be distinguished as very different from lava; and now the disposition of this is to be considered.

'Sometimes it is found in an irregular mass or mountain, as Mr Cronstedt has properly observed; but he has also said, that this is not the case in general. His words are: "It is oftener found in veins in mountains of another kind, running commonly in a serpentine manner contrary or across the direction of the rock itself." '

This quotation is taken from Cronstedt's English edition (1770), where it forms part of a description of *The Trap of the Swedes*. Hutton amplifies Cronstedt's statement, which is based on Scandinavia and Germany, by citing some thirty examples each of Scottish dykes and sills of whinstone with markedly transgressive margins. Among the dykes the most noteworthy is an east-west example south of the River Earn on the road to Crieff. 'It is thirty-four yards wide, stands perpendicular; and . . . may be considered as having been traced for twenty or thirty miles . . . perhaps much farther'. The sills are strikingly represented by Salisbury Crags, Edinburgh.

'Having thus described these masses, which have flowed by heat among the strata of the globe, . . . it will now be proper to examine the difference that subsists between these subterraneous lavas, as they may be termed, and the analogous bodies, which are proper lavas, in having issued out of a volcano.

'In the erupted lavas, those substances which are subject to calcine and vitrify in our fires, suffer similar changes, when delivered from a compression which had rendered them fixed, though in an extremely heated state. Thus, a lava in which there is much calcareous spar› when it comes to be exposed to the atmosphere, or delivered from the compressive force of its confinement, effervesces by the explosion of its fixed air; . . .

'In the body of our whinstone on the contrary, there is no mark of calcination or vitrification. We frequently find in it (especially in the amydaloidal type) much calcareous spar, or *terra calcarea aerata,* which had been in a melted state by heat, and had been crystallized by congelation into a sparry form . . . The specimens of this kind, which I have from the whinstone or prophyry rock of the Calton-hill, exhibit every species of mineral operation, in forming jasper, figured agate, and marble; and they demonstrate that this had been performed by heat or fusion.'

Hutton introduces two comparisons with more southerly localities on the Continent, comparisons which are of interest in themselves, apart from their misapplication to the complex problem he has tackled. The first is based upon a quotation from Guy S. T. de Dolomieu (1750–1801), after whom the Dolomites of the Tyrol are named. The second concerns Sir William Hamilton (1730–1803), Nelson's friend, and a keen investigator of Vesuvius and Etna.

Dolomieu in Faujas de Saint Fond's *Minéralogie des Volcans* had maintained that in Sicily all submarine lavas carry zeolite-filled amygdales, whereas all subaerial lavas carry empty vesicles; while Hamilton informed Hutton, when shown 'those mineral veins and spars in our whinstone, that he had never observed the like in lavas'.

Hutton's contrast between the northern whins of Scotland, etc., and the southern lavas of Auvergne, etc., posed, rather than settled, a problem. Nowadays the differences which he recognised can largely be attributed to relative youth of the southern volcanoes, which has allowed them to retain empty vesicles and easily recognisable cone-and-crater forms, with relatively little exposure of underground plan, and also with relatively little decomposition of substance.

Owing to his super-insistence upon the abundance of intrusions among the igneous rocks of Scotland and other northern countries, Hutton came to be known among his contemporaries as the originator and leader of the so-called Plutonists—a name, Playfair tells us, introduced by his enemy Kirwan. Hutton was, of course, right in claiming that many whinstones have transgressive contacts and coarser-than-lava texture; but he was wrong in thinking that content of amygdales is an intrusive character. It is in fact very much the reverse.

Hutton and his devoted admirer, Playfair, both found considerable satisfaction in the thought that Plutonic philosophy differs considerably from Vulcanic [Volcanic] philosophy. They are, however, two parts of a natural whole. Igneous rocks, which have consolidated underground are Plutonic, in the original sense, irrespective of texture; while those which have been ejected at the surface are volcanic. This is admirably admitted by Playfair in spite of his desire to defend as far as possible the originality of his friend's conceptions. 'When', says he, 'instead of a heated vapour, melted matter is thrown up through the *shafts* or *tubes,* which thus communicate with the mineral regions, veins of whinstone or basaltes are formed in the interior of the earth. When the melted matter reaches to the surface, it is thrown out in the form of lava, and all the phenomena of volcanoes are produced'.

It is curious that Hutton's division between a northern province of whinstone and a southern one of proper-lava corresponds, broadly speaking, with an original chemical contrast. The rocks in the north, with which he was mainly concerned, tend to be less alkaline than the rocks he read about in the south—there is, for instance, nothing in Britain like the leucitic ash that overwhelmed Pompeii. When microscopic petrology came into being, the great German masters of classification mistook this local phenomenon for one of world-wide significance. They used two sets of names, the one for pre-Tertiary rocks (the whinstone set), and the other for Tertiary and later rocks (the Auvergne set). This idea was not wholly abandoned until 1892, when Frederick H. Hatch, working under Harry Rosenbusch, described a Carboniferous nepheline-phonolite from Traprain Law in East Lothian. Nepheline-phonolite had long been thought to be exclusively Tertiary or post-Tertiary.

'Part IV. System of Decay and Renovation observed in the Earth'

Hutton starts Part IV with a restatement of his Uniformitarian outlook: 'There is no occasion for having recourse to any unnatural supposition of evil, to any destructive accident in nature, or to the agency of any preternatural cause, in explaining that which naturally appears'. In other words, there is no need to invoke catastrophes.

To this, a little later, Hutton adds some very wholesome advice: 'We are not to limit nature with the uniformity of an equable progression. . . . It is our business to learn of nature (that is by observation) the ways and means, which in her wisdom are adopted.'

Meanwhile he repeats much that has already been argued in Parts I–III, with, however, a welcome expansion in regard to geological time. 'We are not to suppose that there is any violent exertion of power, such as is required in order to produce a great event in little time; in nature, we find no deficiency in respect of time'.

Erosion, he explains, continually changes the face of the earth. 'We never see a river in flood, but we must acknowledge the carrying away of part of our land, to be sunk at the bottom of the sea; we never see a storm upon the coast, but we are informed of a hostile attack of the sea upon our country; attacks which must in time wear away the bulwarks of our soil, and sap the foundations of our buildings. Thus great things are not understood without the analysing of many operations, and the combination of time with many events happening in succession.'

The operation which Hutton considers most likely to supply a measure of erosion in terms of years is the assault of the sea against our coasts during the humanly recorded time that separates our own days from those of the classical Greeks and Romans. His conclusion is as follows:

'To sum up the argument, we are certain that all the coasts of the present continents are wasted by the sea, and constantly wearing away upon the whole; but this operation is so extremely slow, that we cannot find a measure of the quantity in order to form an estimate. Therefore, the present continents of the earth, which we consider as in a state of perfection, would, in the natural operations of the globe, require time indefinite for their destruction.'

So, after recognising a 'succession of worlds established in a system of nature', Hutton closes what may be called the first edition of his *Theory of the Earth* with the resounding phrase:

'The result, therefore, of our present enquiry is, that we find no vestige of a beginning—no prospect of an end'.

Chapter 6

1785-1788
GREAT EXPLORATIONS

THE PRESENT chapter covers field-work from 1785 to 1788, two dates that are already familiar. During 1785, Hutton presented the first edition of his *Theory of the Earth* (see pp. 32–50) to the Royal Society of Edinburgh; and during 1788 this Society published it in Volume I of its *Transactions*.

Six explorations of the 1785 to 1788 period show Hutton in a particularly good light. He stands out as a field-geologist interpreting granites and unconformities. His observations strengthened enormously certain fundamental deductions which he had already put forward, explicitly and implicitly, in the 1785 MS. of his *Trans. R.S.E.* paper. Accordingly, one would have expected him to add an appendix announcing the good news; but no! The only alteration in the 1788 version appears to have been the change of sub-title.

Here is an instance of Hutton's failure to take advantage of delay in publication. In his *Theory* as printed in 1788, there is no reference to his discovery of granite veins: in Glen Tilt, 1785; Galloway, 1786; or Arran, 1787—see below.

This carelessness (in the literal sense of the word) was habitual; and has recently been discussed by Sergei Ivanovich Tomkeieff in Volume III of the *Proc. Geol. Assn.*, 1962—see pp. 80, 82. Tomkeieff is concerned with unconformities, and his argument, very slightly modified, runs as follows. Hutton, in Chapters I–V of Volume I of his 1795 book, makes no mention of his observations of *seen,* as contrasted with *inferred,* unconformities, which he had found: in Arran, 1787; along the Jed, 1787; or at Siccar Point, 1788 (see below). Tomkeieff therefore suggests that Hutton sent his chapters to the printer as they were written, even if authorship was spread over a number of years. This seems the only possible explanation, if we replace *printer* by *amanuensis;* and virtual confirmation is afforded by a note which Tomkeieff quotes from the end of Hutton's Chapter

V: 'Since writing this chapter', Hutton says, 'I am enabled to speak more decisively upon that point [dealing with angular unconformity] having acquired more light upon the subject, as will appear in the next chapter'.

Hutton and Playfair, though they spoke and wrote freely about the *idea* of unconformity, never used the *word* itself. Tomkeieff points out all the same that this can be traced back to 1594 in relation to theology, where it has long since been replaced by *non-conformity*. Transferred into geology, Tomkeieff first finds it in Robert Jameson's 1805 description of the County of Dumfries, serving there, in all probability, as a translation of Werner's *abweichende Lagerung,* literally *deviating bedding*.

Hutton's *idea* of what we now call unconformity had many *facets*. Among them one was universal, namely recognition of *erosion* separating the deposition of an older from that of a younger formation. In the examples which gave Hutton so much delight, this erosion was particularly clear, because it followed folding of the older formations concerned. The localities mentioned above afforded exposures of what is now called *angular unconformity;* and it was for such that the name *unconformity* was introduced. However, the general application of the term was soon extended to cover non-angular unconformities, in the definition of which intervening erosion is taken as the *sine qua non*. This introduces the complicated notion of major, minor and trivial unconformities, with the latter in profusion in current-bedded strata—but in actual practice one need not mention everything, always. It is often quite understandable to speak of a conformable sequence, passing over in silence hosts of trivial, and even minor, gaps, treated as local detail.

We have in the above paid no attention to a terrible alternative, *unconformability,* which was commonly used by men of the standing of Smith, Lyell and Geikie. A revolt about the turn of the century has fortunately driven it into limbo.

1785 *Glen Tilt*

Hutton recalls how, when in 1785 he had presented his *Theory,* he had been uncertain as to whether granite resulted from fusion of sediment *in place,* or whether in its molten state it had *intruded* itself upwards, as whinstone and porphyry have so clearly done.

Some imperfect descriptions of granite veins already existed in the literature, for instance by Buffon in the Limoges and de Saussure in the Valorcine; but Hutton determined to study the subject for himself, considering that this would offer the severest test possible of his views.

Hutton thought, from what was known of the country, that some of the streams of the Tay drainage near Blair Atholl were likely to provide critical junction-exposures of granite and schist. Accordingly he and Clerk of Eldin decided to find the contact 'whatever the distance the pursuit might lead them among the mountains of this elevated tract'. Having mentioned their intention to the Duke of Atholl, they were invited to accompany him into Glen Tilt, which they did in the summer of 1785.

'In this undertaking', says Hutton in a preliminary note to the Royal Society of Edinburgh (read 1790, published in vol. iii of the same, 1794), 'I have succeeded beyond my most flattering expectations. . . . Little did we imagine that we should be so fortunate as to meet with the object of our search upon the very spot where the Duke's hunting seat is situate, and where we were entertained with the utmost hospitality and elegance'. In the clean-washed river bed we 'had every satisfaction that it was possible to desire, having found the most perfect evidence, that the granite had been made to break the Alpine strata, and invade the country in a fluid state.'

Hutton published excellent illustrations by Clerk, but reserved fuller treatment for the third volume of his book on his *Theory*. This as we have seen, did not appear till 1899; but fortunately the story is very happily, albeit briefly, expanded in Playfair's *Biographical Account,* 1803, based here on the testimony of Clerk. 'When they had reached Forest Lodge, about seven miles up the valley, Dr Hutton already found himself in the midst of the objects which he wished to examine. In the bed of the river many veins of red granite (no less, indeed, than six large veins in the course of a mile), were seen traversing the black micaceous schistus, and producing by the contrast of colour, an effect that might be striking even to an unskilful observer. The sight of objects which verified at once many important conclusions in his system, filled him with delight; and as his feelings, on such occasions, were always strongly expressed, the guides who accompanied him, were convinced that it must be nothing less than the discovery of a vein of silver or gold, that would call forth such strong marks of joy and exultation.'

Hutton in his 1794 announcement did not mention the continuity of the veins with any major mass of granite; and Playfair, who visited the locality before writing on the subject in his *Illustrations,* 1802, thought at the time that this had not been established. However, in his *Biographical Account,* 1803, he took the opportunity of recording Clerk's assurance that 'on the north side of the glen [there is] a mass of granite to which the veins can be directly traced'.

1786 *Galloway*

Hutton and Clerk of Eldin were now eager to see the junction which they knew must lie at the head of Loch Doon in the Southern Uplands. They were extremely fortunate in finding exposures at Cairnsmore of Fleet, about 2½ miles from Ferrytown of Cree, and again midway between Covend and Saturness Point of the Solway. Once more they were completely satisfied, for the granite has 'broken and floated the schistus in every way possible', and has injected itself in 'small veins between the stratified bodies'. Hutton deferred main publication in the same way as in regard to Glen Tilt.

Turning to Playfair's *Biographical Account,* we read: 'One of those junctions was afterwards very carefully examined by Sir James Hall and Mr Douglas, now Lord Selkirk, who made the entire circuit of a tract of granite country, which reaches from the banks of Loch Ken, where the junction is best seen, westward to the valley of Penure, occupying a space of about 11 miles by 7. See *Edinburgh Transactions,* vol. iii. *History,* p. 8.' This is the same 1794 volume as that which holds Hutton's preliminary note.

Hall's account just quoted was published in 1794 in abstract only. Full publication was deferred till 1798, the year after Hutton's death. The reason was that the paper introduced experiments, which latter Hutton mistrusted. Actually Hall's work provided guidance of the highest value. It treated igneous melts as solutions, and emphasized the importance of slow cooling as illustrated 'by an accidental experiment . . . which had happened at one of Leith Glass-houses a few weeks previous to the reading of this paper. A quantity of common green glass having been allowed, in a great mass, to cool gradually and very slowly, it was found to have lost all the properties of glass, being opaque, white, very hard and refractory, and wholly composed of a set of crystals'. This led Hall to an explanation of porphyritic texture depending upon generation of large crystals formed under conditions of very slow cooling, which later became embedded in a multitude of small crystals due to exposure of the residual melt to much more rapid cooling.

1787 *Arran*

On the first of August, 1787, Hutton visited Arran along with John, son of Clerk of Eldin. They found abundant granite veins at three localities, and brought home specimens weighing some hundredweights. These satisfied all who examined them.

Hutton's conclusion, reached in Glen Tilt, Galloway and Arran, and assembled in the preliminary publication of 1794, was that granite is later than associated schistus. It is not, of course, later than such secondary strata as have been deposited unconformably upon its eroded surface.

It so happens that it was in Arran, 1787, that Hutton found his first example of an *exposed* unconformity—in this case between schist and Old Red Sandstone (often called Carboniferous). We need not anticipate what further we shall have to say in Chapter 10f.

Other objects of interest which attracted Hutton's attention during this visit were the abundance of pudding-stone, the multitude of whinstone dykes and the presence of pitchstone intrusions. He used often to say that he had nowhere found his expectations 'so much exceeded as in the grand and instructive appearances with which nature has adorned this little island'.

1787 *Jedburgh*

In the autumn of the same year, 1787, while on a visit to a friend, Hutton found another exposure of Secondaries resting unconformably on Primaries, this time in the banks of the Jed, about a mile upstream from Jedburgh. Here Old Red Sandstone lies flatly upon steeply tilted Silurian greywacke with a thin intervening band of pudding-stone. Hutton, to use his own words, 'was soon satisfied in regard to this phenomenon, and rejoiced at [his] good fortune in stumbling upon an object so interesting to the general history of the earth, and which [he] had been long looking for in vain'. (See Chapter 8f.)

1788 *Siccar Point*

Next year, 1788, Hutton set out to find an exposure of the Jedburgh unconformity nearer to his old home at Sligh Houses. Streams in the neighbourhood were successfully searched; but the outstanding foray of the campaign was a landing made at Siccar Point, 6 miles east of Dunglass. Hutton, along with Sir James Hall and Playfair, took a boat at Dunglass Burn, and in perfect weather hugged the cliffbound shore as far as St. Abbs Head. Hutton tells of how they found midway, at Siccar Point, 'a beautiful picture of the junction washed bare by the sea'.

What follows in his 1794 account is adequate; but it appears that he was not overwhelmed, having already been feasted in Arran and near Jedburgh. In fact he considered an inland exposure of very thick pudding-stone to be 'an object far more interesting in our eyes.... We returned perfectly satisfied; and Sir James Hall is to pursue this subject farther when he shall be in those mountains shooting muir-game'.

Hutton's companions, however, showed no signs of blaséness, as the following much quoted description from Playfair's *Biographical Account* clearly illustrate:

'Dr Hutton was highly pleased with appearances that set in so clear a light the different formations of the parts which compose the exterior crust of the earth, and where all the circumstances were combined that could render the observation satisfactory and precise. On us who saw these phenomena for the first time, the impression made will not easily be forgotten. The palpable evidence presented to us, of one of the most extraordinary and important facts in the natural history of the earth, gave a reality and substance to those theoretical speculations, which, however probable, had never till now been directly authenticated by the testimony of the senses. We often said to ourselves, what clearer evidence could we have had of the different formation of these rocks, and of the long interval which separated their formation, had we actually seen them emerging from the bottom of the deep? We felt ourselves necessarily carried back to the time when the schistus on which we stood was yet at the bottom of the sea, and when the sandstone before us was only beginning to be deposited, in the shape of sand or mud, from the waters of a superincumbent ocean. An epocha still more remote presented itself, when even the most ancient of these rocks, instead of standing upright in vertical beds, lay in horizontal planes at the bottom of the sea, and was not yet disturbed by that immeasurable force which has burst asunder the solid pavement of the globe. Revolutions still more remote appeared in the distance of this extraordinary perspective*. The mind seemed to grow giddy by looking so far into the abyss of time; and while we listened with earnestness and admiration to the philosopher who was unfolding to us the order and series of these wonderful events, we became sensible of how much farther reason may sometimes go than imagination may venture to follow. As for the rest, we were truly fortunate in the course we had pursued in this excursion; a great number of curious and important facts presented themselves, and we returned having collected in one day, more ample materials for future speculation, than have sometimes resulted from years of diligent and laborious research'.

As a direct result of the Siccar Point exploration, Playfair made a series of trips with the Right Honourable Lord Webb Seymour to locate similar exposures in widely separated parts of Great Britain. The list set out in his *Illustrations* is quite impressive.

Here it may be pointed out that several individuals of at least three generations of the landed aristocracy of Great Britain took a lively interest in the developing science of geology. It added, as it were, new dimensions of depth and time to the ground beneath their feet; it sometimes brought to light astounding fossils, such as the giant reptiles of the Weald and Lyme Regis; at others, it introduced exciting problems, in simple terms which could be understood, concerning such matters as the origin of granite; at others again, it might penetrate to a hidden coalfield or some other source of mineral wealth. The geologists of the time were mostly men of means with considerable leisure; but not, as a rule, in a position to find accommodation and transport in out of the way districts.

* 'For a fuller deduction of the conclusions here referred to, see *Theory of the Earth*, Vol. 1, p. 458; also *Illustrations of the Huttonian Theory*, p. 113.'

1788 *Isle of Man*

In the latter part of the summer of 1788, the Duke of Atholl took Hutton and Clerk of Eldin to the Isle of Man to make a mineral survey. What they 'saw there, however, was not much calculated to illustrate any of the great facts in geology.' The excursion 'in other respects was very agreeable . . . and they again experienced the politeness and hospitality' they had enjoyed three years previously in Glen Tilt.

At first sight the choice of the Isle of Man may seem unexpected; but it must be realised that until 1764 the island was under the sovereignty of the family of Atholl. Being exempt from customs duties, it had developed into a vast den frequented by all the smugglers of the west coat of Scotland. In 1764, George Clerk (p. 7) was appointed by the British Government to report on means to correct this situation. Clerk's advice was to purchase the sovereignty of the island. Finances were low, and for some time the government sought to meet the difficulty by increasing the number of cruisers on the station. Eventually, however, they adopted Clerk's plan on finding that their own would prove the more expensive.

Chapter 7

1788-1795
DIVERSIFIED INTERESTS

DURING THE years of great exploration, Hutton was hard at work on several different subjects besides geology. It so happened that a number of these arrived at publication between 1788 and 1795.

1788 *Climate*

In 1784 Hutton read a paper on a *Theory of Rain* before the Royal Society of Edinburgh, and it was published in 1788. The theory was based upon the observation that one's breath on a cold day is often rendered misty by condensation. Hutton considered that this followed mixing of the expired air with the external air; and he invoked mixing of air currents as the main cause of condensation in the atmosphere at large, and consequently of rain. He supported this interpretation by a global review of the incidence of wind and rain. Nowadays, it must be admitted, such admixture is regarded as of very minor importance in rain production.

Quite apart, however, from meteorological applications, we may note that Hutton drew an interesting physical inference from his commonplace observation of condensation. He concluded, quite correctly, that the amount of water-vapour which air can carry increases increasingly rapidly as the temperature rises.

This conclusion of Hutton's was soon vigorously attacked by Jean André de Luc, the originator of the word *geology*. De Luc (1727–1817) came of a distinguished Genevan family; but, after taking his share in local political struggles, he migrated to England, 1773. Here he was appointed Reader to Queen Charlotte. A better title, perhaps, would have been Writer, for he addressed to his patroness a long educative series of letters which were presently published and republished in collected form. He invented an ingenious hygrometer and did valuable work on electricity. He was also the first to publish on latent heat, regarding which its discoverer Joseph Black had been content merely to lecture. De Luc's great desire was to bring the facts of science into harmony with Holy Writ. His most important geological work was: *Physical and Moral Letters on the History of the Earth, and of Man* (1778, enlarged 1779). He opposed Hutton on many matters. Here we are concerned with his attempt to refute the physical principle upon which Hutton based his *Theory of Rain.* Hutton's first reaction was a far-too-long paper in *Trans R.S.E.,* vol. ii, 1790, entitled: *Answers to Objections of M. de Luc with regard to the Theory of Rain.* Playfair deplored the somewhat bitter nature of the controversy, and thought that Hutton, being obviously right, might have been a little more gentle.

We have already noted in Chapter 2 some of Hutton's other climatic observations. Playfair credits him with the explanation of the upward decrease of atmospheric temperature as connected with cooling due to expansion. I am very doubtful if this claim can be maintained. Hutton's account of the connexion does not appear in his *Theory of Rain* as read in 1784, though it is included in *The Theory of Rain Further Illustrated and Objections Answered,* in his *Dissertations* of 1792 (see below). The connexion between atmospheric temperature and pressure had meanwhile been demonstrated by Erasmus Darwin in *Frigorific Experiments in the Mechanical Expansion of Air,* read 1787, and published in the *Philosophical Transactions,* 1788.

Among Hutton's unpublished contributions to meteorology, Playfair notes his moistening the bulb of a thermometer to obtain a lowering of temperature which could provide a measure of atmospheric humidity. In other words he invented a hygrometer quite different from de Luc's.

1788 *Natural History of Writing*

In the first volume of *Trans. R.S.E.,* 1788, Hutton deals broadly, and also in some detail, with the subject of writing. He acknowledges the international value of the *verbal* style used by the Chinese as opposed to the *elemental* or *alphabetical* style adopted by most other nations; but he realises that the former 'would require to make it the business of a man's life to read and write'.

He then proceeds to connect each sound that is used in speech with a particular symbol—usually one of the letters of the English alphabet; and he makes a strong plea to purge from our own system of writing its many non-phonetic absurdities. In the course of this appeal, Hutton appositely points out that divergence from phoneticism in alphabetic writing is a partial adoption of the verbal style of China—but without any corresponding advantage. Instead, it introduces unrewarding difficulties for those who are learning to write and read, both at home and abroad.

In a metaphysical book of 1794 (see below), Hutton returns to what Playfair calls the *Natural History of Language*. It greatly occupied his thoughts, and was the subject of several unpublished manuscripts.

1790-1791 *Attacks by de Luc*

The publication of the Royal Society of Edinburgh's edition of the *Theory of the Earth,* 1788, attracted very little comment, appreciative or the reverse, outside of Edinburgh. However, in the *Monthly Review* for 1790 and 1791, de Luc launched a series of spirited attacks. Hutton at the time published no reply, though it is thought that he wrote one for the *Review,* which was not accepted. We shall therefore defer consideration to Chapter 8c, where one will find how he dealt with the matter, free from censorship.

1792 *Dissertations on Different Subjects in Natural Philosophy*

When Playfair came to know Hutton, about 1781, the latter had already completed an M.S. on Chemistry, Physics and Metaphysics. This was much the same as the *Dissertations* which he published in 1792 under the title given above. Among the various subjects discussed we may concentrate here upon phlogiston (p. 1). Though himself a phlogistonist, Hutton was delighted with the experiments on the calcination of metals, which, since 1775, had led to anti-phlogistonist theories. Both he and Lavoisier claimed that the full equation for the development of water from hydrogen and oxygen could be written:

$$\text{Hydrogen} + \text{Oxygen} = \text{Water} + x,$$

where x by Hutton was called *phlogiston,* and by Lavoisier *calorique.*

The difference was more than nominal when one considers the supposed source of the x. Hutton derived it from the hydrogen; Lavoisier from the oxygen. Hutton regarded the liberated phlogiston as imponderable matter which escaped detection by the balance, but was none the less essential on that account. (I suppose nowadays that the liberated energy could theoretically be assigned a mass equivalent.) On the general merits of the case, I need say no more, because they have been expertly handled by J. R. Partington and D. McKie in the 1937–38 volumes of *Annals of Science*. On the other hand, it seems profitable to indicate why Hutton clung to phlogistic principles with great tenacity. In the first place, of course, he took the common view of phlogistonists that it is the combustible bodies that are mainly concerned with combustion—admittedly a one-sided conception, but few at that time had seen oxygen burning in hydrogen. In the second place, being a farmer at heart, he recognised the overwhelming importance of the *physiological cycle,* in which: (1) *animals* consume part of their substance in conjunction with oxygen of the air to give water and carbonic acid; while (2) *plants* in their green leaves receive 'solar substance' from the light of the sun, and with its help regenerate organic matter from water and carbonic acid. 'The solar matter', he says in his *Dissertations,* 'when compounded in an inflammable body, is phlogiston; and when restored to its former liberty, to its natural motion, is light'. It is also 'commutable', and may equally well appear as heat.

It is curious that Hutton, while recognising the sun as indispensable to the continuity of the earth's life-processes, never expressed concern as to its possible exhaustion. It scarcely seems adequate to say: 'From natural appearances, the past duration of this world is traced for a space of time that is indefinite. . . . The consequence of this reasoning is evidently to confirm our notion with respect to the wisdom of nature; and to strengthen the presumption that natural bodies must have the power of acquiring phlogistic matter in proportion to the necessary waste of this useful substance in the economy of the world'.

Hutton was led to physics by his interest in chemistry and mineralogy. His speculations as set out in his 1792 *Dissertations* contain scarcely anything of permanent value. For instance, he argues that, if we agree that *matter makes bodies,* we must not assume that *matter has the same properties as bodies,* for this would reduce our former statement to *matter makes matter,* which is not worth saying. This enables him to maintain that matter need not have inertia and gravity, which, of course, is in keeping with his view that phlogiston is an imponderable form of matter.

1793 *Illness*

Hutton was seized with a severe illness in the summer of 1793. Previously he had been healthy and active in body and mind. The disorder (a retention of urine) threatened his life; and he had to undergo a dangerous and painful operation. He was very weak and confined to his room for several months. Gradually, however, he picked up to reasonable health, much better than expected. At this stage he found amusement in seeing a book on metaphysics, now briefly to be examined, through the press.

1794 *Investigation of the Principles of Knowledge and the Progress of Reason from Sense to Science and Philosophy*

By the time I had struggled through Hutton's *Dissertations* on Physics, 1792, I found myself so exhausted that I took his three volumes of *Investigation* into metaphysics, 1794, on trust from Playfair.

Apparently Hutton realised that in such phrases as *red rose* and *red light* we use the word red in quite distinct though connected meanings. Some of us think that language, in its unconscious growth, has adopted a justifiable economy of words. We judge the meaning of *red,* for instance, not from the word alone, but also in part from its context. Hutton took a different view, when metaphysically inclined. Red, for him, could have only one meaning; and if we admit that light can be red, then what we usually call a red rose is really a rose which diffuses red light when illuminated with white light. Reasoning in this fashion, Hutton reached conclusions which Playfair summarised as follows: 'In a word, external things are no more like the perceptions they give rise to, than wine is similar to intoxication, or opium to the delirium which it produces'. Playfair compares Hutton's metaphysics with that of George Berkeley (1685–1753). Hutton held that there was external existence, though things are not what they seem. Berkeley held that there was no external existence, apart from the Deity. Playfair was certain that Berkeley would have come to Hutton's position, if he had been better acquainted with physics, and had 'made it more a rule to exclude all hypothesis'. At the same time he admitted sadly that he had 'hardly found this work of Dr Hutton's quoted by any writer of eminence, except by Dr Par, in his *Spital sermon,* a tract no less remarkable for its learning and acuteness, than for the liberality and candour of the sentiments which it contains'.

Playfair further points out that 'Dr Hutton has taken great pains to deduce from his system, in a regular manner, the leading doctrines of morality, and natural religion, having dedicated the third volume of his book almost wholly to that object', and that, while thus employed, he writes with unwonted 'perspicuity', so that 'the warmth of his benevolent and moral feelings bursts through the clouds that so often veil from us the clearest of his understanding. One, in particular, deserves notice, in which he treats of the importance of the female character to society in a state of high civilization.'

1794 *Kirwan's Onslaught*

During the convalescent stage of his 1793 illness, Hutton was further invigorated by a whole-hearted attack by Richard Kirwan of Dublin. It took the form of a paper in the *Trans. R. Irish Acad.,* 1794, entitled: *Examination of the Supposed Igneous Origin of Stony Substances.* Kirwan was a distinguished chemist and mineralogist, destined soon to become President of the Academy, and already leader of the local Neptunists. In this last connexion he is best remembered for his mistaken acceptance of fossils in a basaltic intrusion near Portrush in the north of Ireland. This was in 1799, two years after Hutton's death. The fossils were genuine enough; but the enclosing rock proved not to be basalt when specimens were examined in Edinburgh by Playfair, Lord Seymour and Sir James Hall. Instead, they occurred in hard-baked Liassic shale, separated by an abrupt contact from adjacent chilled basalt.

The main features of Kirwan's 1794 paper may be summarised as follows, numbered successively 1–5:

(1) *Kirwan minimised* weathering of solid rock to soil; river trans-

port of soil from mountain to sea; and coastal erosion. Accordingly he dismissed Hutton's question, *by what means may a decayed world be renovated,* as superfluous.

(2) *He also minimised* the proportion of solid stratified rocks, which may, even possibly, be regarded by people of good sense as having been deposited on the sea bottom in the form of unconsolidated *gravel, sand* and *argillaceous* and *calcareous strata.* Hutton had included in this category most crystalline schists and unfossiliferous marbles; but Kirwan excluded these, presumably because he thought it obvious that they owe their condition to *contemporaneous,* rather than *subsequent* consolidation (see p. 71). Contemporaneous consolidation he attributed to oceanic precipitation of matrix among diffuse mutually-attractive subsiding particles. As granite was for him an oceanic chemical precipitate, it probably seemed natural to him occasionally to use the word granitic in a very broad sense including stratified schist and unfossiliferous marble. This would account for his statement that 'the basis of the greater part of Scotland is evidently a granitic rock'. I mention this because we shall on p. 70 find Hutton treating the remark as a stupid mistake.

Kirwan makes it clear that, in his opinion, Hutton's conception of subsequent consolidation arises partly 'from the author's own gratuitous supposition, that strata existed at the bottom of the sea previously to their consolidation; a circumstance which will not be allowed by the patrons of the aqueous origin of stony substances'. If there is no subsequent consolidation, there is, of course, no point in Hutton's explanation of it as a result of combined operation of heat and pressure.

(3) *Unlike Hutton,* Kirwan very seldom introduced religion into the argument developed in this paper—though from what has been written by his detractors one would imagine the reverse. At one point, however, he does impatiently ask: 'Why should we suppose this habitable earth to arise from the ruins of another anterior to it, contrary to reason and the tenor of the mosaic history?' While on the next page he complains that Hutton plunges into an abyss of time, 'from which human reason recoils', and in which, to make use of his own expression, *'we find no vestige of a beginning'.* That is all; and yet Playfair in his *Principles* devotes pages to the defence of his friend's memory in this very connexion. He tells us, for instance,

that Kirwan 'endeavoured to load Hutton's *Theory* with the reproach of atheism and impiety', and that, 'in bringing forward this harsh and ill-founded censure, he was neither animated by the spirit nor guided by the maxims of the true philosophy'. One feels that Playfair exaggerated.

(4) *Kirwan was* mistaken in supposing that Hutton attributed the internal heat of the world to combustion; but this was Hutton's fault for careless use of words (pp. 5, 41, 68).

(5) *The last point* that Kirwan tackles is the origin of *granite*. His treatment is mainly physico-chemical, and he draws special attention to a paper 'by the learned Dr Beddoes in *Philosophical Transactions* for 1791, p. 56, etc.' Beddoes tells us that 'a mixture of different earths, with more or less metallic matter, in returning from a state of fusion to a solid consistence, may assume, sometimes, the homogeneous basaltic, and sometimes the heterogeneous granitic internal structure. No fact is more familiar than that it depends altogether upon the management of the fire, and the time of cooling, whether a mass shall have the uniform vitreous fracture, or an earthy broken grain arising from a confused crystallization'—and he cites Réaumur's porcelain as an example. Kirwan replies that slow cooling allows escape of volatiles, and that this is the governing factor in development of strong texture out of glass.

Here we may interpolate regarding Hall's contribution to this subject, though it takes us forward to 1798, a year after Hutton's death. In 1788 Hall read Hutton's *Theory,* and was induced by its poor presentation 'to reject his system entirely'. However, 'after three years of almost daily warfare', he was softened by Hutton's lucid conversation, and 'began to view his fundamental principles with less and less repugnance'. He started experimental investigation in 1790; but, in deference to Hutton, deferred further action till 1798, the year after Hutton's death. Hutton was afraid of the difference of scale in natural, as contrasted with human, laboratories, despite the fruitful influence which Black's discovery of carbonic acid had had upon his own geological outlook. Very likely he knew by this time that granite-melt in an open crucible cannot be persuaded to recrystallise as granite. At the same time, Hall found that basaltic melt can be consolidated as glass, or as distinctly crystallised rock, according as it is cooled rapidly or slowly.

This conclusion seems to have been accepted very happily by both Plutonists and Neptunists, though, as we have seen, the latter thought that loss of volatiles lay at the root of the matter; and it must be admitted that a granite-melt without water under pressure will never develop a coarse crystallisation. On the other hand, one's respect for Kirwan's judgment gets a rude shock on reading in his final paragraph: 'To close this controversy I shall only add, that granite, recently in the moist way, has frequently been found. . . . Thus a mole, having been constructed in the Oder in the year 1722, 350 feet long, . . . the middle space was filled entirely with granite sand. In a short time this concreted into a substance so compact as to be impenetrable by water.' Hutton's answer will be found on p. 73.

Up to date, Hutton had often been urged by his friends to publish his theory more fully; but with little avail. Now, however, the very day Kirwan's paper was put into his hands, he began to revise his manuscript; and he determined to send it to the press as soon as possible. When two volumes appeared in 1795 it was found that Chapter II of Volume I has been assigned to the refutation of Kirwan's criticism.

Chapter 8

1795
HUTTON'S THEORY OF THE EARTH IN BOOK FORM 'WITH PROOFS AND ILLUSTRATIONS' VOLUME I

'WITH THE EXAMINATION OF DIFFERENT OPINIONS ON THAT SUBJECT'

(The following sub-chapters, 8a–8h, deal in succession with Chapters I–VIII of Hutton's Volume I.)

Chapter 8*a*

HUTTON'S CHAPTER I OF VOLUME I 'FACTS IN CONFIRMATION OF THE THEORY OF ELEVATING LAND ABOVE THE SURFACE OF THE SEA'

Hutton's Chapter I is an almost word for word reproduction of his 1788 paper. Occasional alterations of spelling have been made throughout—for instance, the more Scottish *enquiry* is replaced by the more English *inquiry;* and 7 footnotes and 4 text insertions have been added. (*See* pp. 11–12, 14, 26, 33, 34–42, 88–93, 94–96, 112–118, 138–140, 172–174, 177, according to Hutton's 1795 pagination.) Two of the footnotes concern publications dated 1792, so that we know that Hutton did a certain amount of revision up to that date.

The most important of the added footnotes carries a long quotation from Dolomieu, in which it is argued that natural heat may produce different results from those due to artificial heat, because it is commonly applied for a longer time. Hutton counters as follows: 'the essential difference, however, between the natural heat of the mineral regions, and that which we exert upon the surface of the earth, consists in this; that nature applies heat under circumstances which we are unable to imitate, that is, under such compression as shall prevent the decomposition of the constituent substances, by the separation of the more volatile from the more fixed parts. This is a circumstance which, so far as I know, no chemist or naturalist has hitherto considered; and it is that by which the operations of the mineral regions must certainly be explained.' (See pp. 5, 42, 66.)

One may pass over in silence the contents of the other small additions to the original text, beyond noticing that they include references to de Luc, de Saussure and Dolomieu. What, however, is absolutely amazing is the stark absence of any mention of the results obtained during the great explorations, 1785–1788, reviewed in our Chapter 6. Hutton seems to have been thoroughly satisfied with the presentation of his paper handed in in 1785 and published, 1788; and to have thought that there was no call to hurry up reinforcements. These could be deployed in some later chapter, or indeed in some later volume. At the same time, we must in fairness remember that, when he undertook his final revision for 1795 publication, Hutton was a very ill man.

Chapter 8*b*

HUTTON'S CHAPTER II OF VOLUME I 'AN EXAMINATION OF MR KIRWAN'S OBJECTIONS TO THE IGNEOUS ORIGIN OF STONY SUBSTANCES'

Having reproduced in his Chapter I the whole of his 1788 paper, Hutton starts anew in his Chapter II. His revolutionary *Theory* was bound to 'give offence to naturalists who have espoused an opposite opinion'. One such, namely Richard Kirwan, a 'man of science and respectability, . . . has stated his objections' in 1794, which we have already numbered 1–5 in our Chapter 7. The same numbering is used throughout the present chapter.

(1) *Kirwan had* said that: 'Soil is not constantly carried away by the water'. Hutton replies: 'I have not said that it is *constantly* washed away; for, while it is soil in which plants grow, it is not travelling to the sea, although it is on the road, and must arrive in time. I have said that it is *necessarily* washed away, that is occasionally . . . and while rivers carry the materials of our land, and while the sea impairs the coast, I may be allowed to suppose that this is the actual constitution of the earth.

(2) *The next feature* of Kirwan's attack was his minimising of rocks which may possibly, according to him, be imagined to have consolidated from incoherent material. As pointed out on our p. 65, Kirwan in this matter seems to have used the word *granitic* in a very broad sense to include crystalline schists. If so, Hutton misunderstood him, which would account for his discussion of Kirwan's remarks not seeming very apposite; but at least we may welcome an interesting account of his own wanderings prior to 1785 through England, Scotland and Wales. These brought him into contact with very few real granites: Shap, Peterhead and Aberdeen. It is striking that Hutton, writing Chapter II (our 8b) after Kirwan's onslaught of 1794, makes no mention of what he had seen in Glen Tilt, Galloway and Arran, 1785–1787. He may have thought that, as Kirwan was attacking his 1788 paper, he ought to answer it in terms of that paper, and reserve for a later page comments on the results of his great explorations.

Kirwan's claim that there are many stratified mountains 'in which either sand, gravel, shells, coralline, or crustaceous bodies are never or scarce ever found', and in which consolidation is probably *contemporaneous,* not *subsequent* (see p. 65), is met by Hutton with an excellent appeal to changes, to which Lyell long afterwards gave the name of *metamorphism*. Sedimentary characteristics, he says, may be obliterated 'by mechanical comminution', or 'by chemical operations (whatever these may be, whether by the action of water, or of fire, or of both)'—in modern terminology, by dynamic or thermal metamorphism.

(3) *We have already* noted on p. 65 Playfair's reaction to Kirwan's quotation of Hutton's dictum: *'We find no vestige of a beginning.'* Hutton's own reaction was much the same. To Kirwan's conclusion —'Then this system of successive worlds must have been eternal'—

he replies: 'Such is the logic by which, I suppose, I am to be accused of atheism'. He holds that his critic has read into his words a meaning which was not intended. In fact, 'in tracing back the natural operations which have succeeded each other, and mark to us the course of time past, we come to a period in which we cannot see any farther. This, however, is not the beginning of those operations which proceed in time. . . . My principal anxiety, was to shew how the constitution of this world had been wisely contrived; and this I endeavoured to do, not from supposition or conjecture, but from it answering so effectively the end of its intention, viz., the preserving of animal life, which we cannot doubt of being its purpose'.

Hutton then proceeds to counter-attack Kirwan's explanation of consolidation. He does not seem thoroughly to have understood what Kirwan meant in saying that the existence of strata at the bottom of the sea previous to consolidation is 'a circumstance which will not be allowed by the patrons of the aqueous origin of stony substances'. As we have already pointed out, Kirwan alluded in this pronouncement to *contemporaneous* consolidation in opposition to Hutton's *subsequent* consolidation. Contemporaneous consolidation was a fundamental doctrine among the Neptunists. Whether fully understanding or no, Hutton does give an appropriate answer, saying that he has satisfied himself that there is nothing 'original' in the consolidation of stratified rocks. As 'to the masses that are not stratified', he has 'also given proof that they are not in their original state, such as granite, porphyry, serpentine and basaltes.' That is, consolidation has *followed,* in the one case comminution, in the other fluidity.

(4) *Hutton reminds us* that Kirwan, 'in opposition to the theory of consolidating bodies by fusion, has taken great pains to shew, that I cannot provide materials for such a fire as would be necessary, nor find the means to make it burn had I those materials. . . . Had our author attended to the ocular proof that we have of the actual existence of subterraneous fire, and to the physical demonstration which I have given of the effects of heat in melting mineral bodies, he must have seen that those arguments of his . . . can only shew the error of his reasoning. . . . When first I conceived my theory, naturalists were far from suspecting that basaltic rocks were of volcanic origin; I could not then have employed an argument from these rocks as I may do now, for proving that the fires, which we see almost

daily issuing with such force from volcanos, are a continuation of that active cause which has so evidently been executed in all times, and in all places, so far as have been examined of this earth. . . . I wrote a general theory for the inspection of philosophers, who doubtless will point out its errors; but this requires the study of nature, which is not the work of a day; and in this political age, the study of nature seems to be but little pursued by our philosophers. In the meantime, there are, on the one hand, sceptical philosophers, who think there is nothing certain in nature, because there is misconception in the mind of man; on the other hand, there are many credulous amateurs, who go to nature to be entertained as we go to a pantomime: But there are also superficial reasoning men, who think themselves qualified to write on subjects on which they may have read in books—they think they know those regions of the earth which never can be seen; and they judge of the great operations of the mineral kingdom, from having kindled a fire, and looked into the bottom of a little crucible'.

When we read Hutton lamenting as though from a pulpit that politics were diverting philosophers from the study of nature, we must remember that the French Revolution was running its course, 1789–1795, during which, Lavoisier, for instance, went to the guillotine, 1794.

(5) *Hutton disposes* of Kirwan's claim that granite is an aqueous product in the following three paragraphs:

'I had given, as I thought, a kind of demonstration, from the internal evidence of the stone, that granite had been in the fluid state of fusion, and had concreted by crystallization and congelation from the melted state. This no doubt must be a stumbling block to those who maintain that granite mountains are the primitive parts of our earth. . . . It must also be a great, if not invincible obstacle in the way of the aqueous theory, which thus endeavours to explain those granite veins that are found traversing strata; and therefore necessarily of a posterior formation.

'To remove that obstacle in the way of the aqueous theory, or to carry that theory over the obstacle, which he cannot remove, our author [Kirwan] undertakes to refute my theory with regard to the igneous origin of stony substances by giving an example of granite formed upon the surface by means of water, in what is called the moist way.'

The example mentioned is the mole constructed across the River Oder (p. 67). Hutton spends his next three pages in pointing out that no evidence has been advanced to support the extraordinary claim that here granite rock has been produced by passing water through granite sand. All that Kirwan has told us is that this granite sand 'in a short time concreted into a substance so compact as to be impenetrable by water'. Hutton very reasonably suggests that the sand had become clogged with mud as often happens in a filter bed.

Hutton mentioned granite veins just before turning to consider the Oder mole; but he said nothing that might lead one to suspect that he had already studied examples during his great explorations of 1785–1787. He announced his discoveries in this connexion in a paper published by the Royal Society of Edinburgh in 1794; but he withheld further description for what is now called Volume III of his book, posthumous 1899 (see our Chapter 10).

Chapter 8c

HUTTON'S CHAPTER III OF VOLUME I 'OF PHYSICAL SYSTEMS, AND GEOLOGICAL THEORIES IN GENERAL'

'The opinions of other geologists should be clearly stated, that so a fair comparison may be made of theories which are to represent the system of this earth'. Let us take these 'other geologists' in order of succession as Hutton placed them.

Thomas Burnet (1635–1715), author of the *Sacred History of the Earth,* 1681. 'This surely cannot be considered in any other light than as a dream'.

Benoit de Maillet (1656–1738), who arranged for posthumous publication, 1748, of his *Telliamed* (anagram for de Maillet). 'This is a theory which has something in it like a regular system.' A passage quoted in Kirtley F. Mather and Shirley L. Mason's *Source Book in Geology*, 1939, shows commendable appreciation of fossils. Hutton had remarked that this seems 'better founded than most of that which has been wrote upon the subject.'

Count G. L. Leclerc de Buffon (1707–1788), author of

Epoques de la Nature, 1778. Hutton only considers Buffon's first epoch of nature, during which, the author suggests, that a comet knocked the planets out of the body of the sun. Hutton cannot believe that the earth has 'arisen from the cooling of a lump of melted matter which had belonged to another body.' We must 'consider the power and wisdom that must have been exerted, in the contriving, creating and maintaining this living world which maintains such a variety of plants and animals.'

Jean André de Luc (1727–1817), author of *Lettres Physiques et Morales sur les Montagnes,* 1778, 1779. 'De Luc, in his Theory of the Earth, has given us a history of a disaster which befell this well-contrived world;—a disaster which caused the general deluge. . . . But, surely, general deluges form no part of the theory of the earth; for, the purpose of this earth is evidently to maintain vegetable and animal life, and not to destroy them?'

Here we have an excellent illustration of how subjective a guide the theory of design may prove. Hutton could not bring himself to accept Noah's Flood, 'which, without a miracle, must have undone a system of living beings that are so well adapted to the present state of things'; whereas most Europeans of his day whether educated or uneducated, but admittedly with assistance from revelation, not only believed in the Flood, but actually regarded it as a well planned move to replace bad men by good.

Other Geologists.—After having given the whole of his Chapter II to a consideration of Kirwan, and a couple of pages of his Chapter III, which we are now digesting, to mention of Burnet, Maillet, Buffon and de Luc, Hutton seems to have shrunk from further attempts clearly to state 'the opinions of other geologists', except *en masse*. He probably realised, when he started in earnest, that he had a very imperfect knowledge of the minds of contemporary individuals. Playfair puts it kindly: 'He bestowed but little attention on books of opinion, and theory; and while he trusted to the efforts of his mind for digesting the facts he had obtained from reading or experience, into a system of his own, he was not very anxious, at least till that was accomplished, to be informed of the views which other philosophers had taken of the same subject. He was but little disposed to concede anything to mere authority, and to his indifference to the opinions of former theorists it is probably that his own speculations owed some part, both of their excellencies, and their defects'.

So the rest of his Chapter III, and it is a long rest, makes no mention of any individual geologist, not even Werner or Desmarest! It is a monologue addressed to readers who have already mastered his Chapter I. It is not self-explanatory. It carries practically no new material. It is full of contempt for those who adopt theories that do not enshrine design. The Vulcanists, as well as the Neptunists, come in for censure. Two of their mistakes, according to Hutton, are failure to recognise a connexion between volcanoes and elevation, and readiness to explain amygdales by infiltration into vesicles.

Perhaps the only important advance recorded in Hutton's Chapter III is its author's admission that a water-deposited calcareous body may 'so much resemble mineral marble as to be hardly distinguishable in certain cases'—he had previously maintained that distinction was easy. 'Mineral philosophers [the Neptunists] then, reasoning in the manner of the vulgar, or without analysing the subject to its principle, naturally attribute the formation of the mineral marble to a cause of the same sort; and, that mineral marble being found so intimately connected with all the other mineral bodies, we must necessarily conclude, in reasoning according to the soundest principles, that all those different substances have been concreted in the same manner. Thus, having once departed one step from the path of just investigation, our physical science is necessarily bewildered in a labyrinth of error. Let us then, in re-examining our data, point out where lies that first devious step. . . . Here is the source of their delusion': Water, with disolved 'carbonic acid gas (as it is called)' may, in percolating through 'calcareous substances, become saturated with that solution of marble; and, this solution is what is called a *petrifying water*'. Later, exposed to the atmosphere, it may lose its 'acid gas', so that the 'marble, or calcareous substance, concretes and crystallises, separating from the water in a sparry state'. This sequence of percolation and evaporation, though natural on the surface of the earth, is obviously impossible on the floor of the sea, where Hutton imagined that the general consolidation of sediments takes place.

Chapter 8d

HUTTON'S CHAPTER IV OF VOLUME I 'THE SUPPOSITION OF PRIMITIVE MOUNTAINS REFUTED'

1756, 1787 *Primitive defined and revised*

Playfair in his *Illustrations of the Huttonian Theory,* 1802, tells us that Johann Gottlob Lehmann spoke of Primitive rocks 'as forming the basis of all the great chains of mountains', there constituting 'a separate division of the mineral kingdom'. They were 'parts of the original nucleus of the globe, which had undergone no alteration, but remained now such as they were when first created, . . . prior to all organised matter.'

Lehmann, Director of Prussian mines, died in 1767 when Hutton was 41, Werner 18. His explanatory *Essai d'une Histoire Naturelle des Couches de la Terre* (German 1756, French 1759) had appeared when Hutton was 30, and Werner only 7. Hutton's 1795 attack, considered in the present chapter, was delivered against Lehmann's conception of Primitive. Meanwhile, however, Werner had become acknowledged leader of the Neptunists, and had modified Lehmann's definition. In his *Kurze Klassifikation und Beschreibung der verschiedenen Geburgsarten,* 1787, he regards Primitive rocks, not as original creations, but as crystalline precipitates from a universal primitive ocean.

Playfair further tells us that later 'in the Neptunian system, as improved by Werner, an attempt is made to take off the force of' the criticism that certain rocks, hitherto classed as Primitive, contain fossils, pebbles, etc. This attempt is difficult to date exactly, since Werner taught almost wholly by lectures, rather than the written word. It transferred much of Lehmann's *Primitive* to an *Intermediate* or *Transitional* class. The resultant position may be summarised *imaginatively* as follows:

Hutton: In various places in the Alps and Great Britain your so-called Primitive rocks contain fossils and pebbles. This shows that they formed under present-day conditions, and that their original characters have often been masked by what my successor Lyell will call metamorphism.

Werner: You are right in saying that certain accumulations, which we used to call Primitive, contain fossils and pebbles; but we have reclassified these particular accumulations as Transitional, thus excluding them from the Primitive. The change in our classification illustrates the growing pains one must expect in a developing system. We do not accept what you say about metamorphism. Consolidation was often attended by crystallisation in our Primitive, Transitional, and to a less degree Secondary strata. It is an original, not a later character. We believe in an evolutionary system, in which the characters of our world-wide stratigraphical formations have been controlled by the vicissitudes in depth and composition of our Universal Ocean, continuously present from Primitive times till today. The high dips so often seen in rocks have been preserved as a result of immediate consolidation of more or less crystalline accumulations. We do not admit them as evidence of earth-movement.

Hutton: We disbelieve the extraordinary immediate-consolidation characteristics you attribute to the deposits of your universal ocean in its youth, just as completely as you disbelieve our ideas of thermal metamorphism and elevation.

The insertion of Transitional times between Primitive and Secondary helped considerably in the interpretation of local stratigraphical successions; but it introduced big mistakes when correlations were attempted from region to region. Thus, if we consider only the upper limit of the group, Transitional in Scotland, Lakeland and Wales meant, roughly speaking, pre-Devonian; in Cornwall, Devon and Saxony, pre-Permian; in much of Switzerland, pre-Pliocene. This complication resulted from the successive development of the Caledonian, Hercynian and Alpine chains —a matter quite unsuspected by geological disputants in Hutton's day.

1795 *Unstratified Granite*

Hutton discusses the origin of true granite, regarded by Neptunists and Vulcanists as Primitive whether by creation or precipitation. He quotes from de Saussure appearances which lead him, but not de Saussure, to an interpretation involving igneous intrusion. He also mentions 'a specimen from this country [Scotland] of a vein of granite in a granite stone of coarser texture'. Then follows an illuminating foot-note.

'This is what I had wrote upon the subject of granite, before I had acquired such ample testimony from my own observations upon this species of rock. I have given some notice in the 3rd vol. of the Transactions of the Edinburgh R.S. concerning the general result of those observations, which will be given particularly in the course of this work'. The observations were, of course, those made in Glen Tilt, Galloway and Arran, 1785–1788!—See our Chapter 6.

1774-1792 *Fossils in so-called Primitive Rocks*

Hutton found fossils in Wales, probably during his 1774 trip, in rocks of generally admitted Primitive character. 'Thus', he says, 'I had formed my opinion in regard to this alledged fact before I had seen any description either of the Alps or Pyrennean mountains'. The 'alledged fact' was Lehmann's statement that fossils are absent from Primitive rocks. Hutton next quotes similar examples from the Alps, of which he had subsequently read.

Then come full and extraordinarily interesting accounts of discoveries of fossils in 'Primitive' rocks in England and Scotland:

1788, south of Lake Windermere by Hutton
1791, north of Lake Windermere by Playfair
1792, in Tweedale by Sir James Hall.

1777, 1794 *Pallas' Observations on the Formation of Mountains*

Peter Simon Pallas (1741–1811) was a German by birth, who became celebrated for his splendid scientific explorations in Russia and Siberia (1768–1774; 1793–1794), partly planned by the Empress Catherine II. His geological publications are dated 1777 and 1794.

Pallas, grouped the rocks, which in Russia outcrop progressively westwards from the Urals, as belonging to three successive mountains: Primitive, Secondary and Tertiary.

The *Primitive* rocks are described as unfossiliferous; apparently often affected by 'the most violent fire'; rich in mineral veins; and exhibiting transitions from granite to schist.

The *Secondary* mountains are much lower than the Primitive, though their oldest members rest upon the latter. They consist at first of solid and uniform limestone, with steep dips and few fossils. Westwards, this limestone flattens, and often carries abundant marine shells and corals.

The *Tertiary* mountains (presumably Permian to Quaternary, in modern language) are based upon the Secondary limestone, and are formed largely of horizontal sandstone and marl. They contain very scanty marine fossils, but many terrestrial forms. The latter include tree trunks, and, in the uppermost beds, amazingly abundant remains of elephant, rhinoceros and monstrous buffalo.

Hutton's main concern was to argue that several differentiating features, which Pallas took to be original in separating his Primitive, Secondary and Tertiary formations, might well be referred to subsequent earth-movement, intrusion and metamorphism.

Hutton also, very naturally, was greatly interested in the breath-taking elephant fauna. He decided that elephant and rhinoceros had formerly lived in Siberia, and that Pallas was wrong in supposing they had been swept in by a torrent from far-away India. 'Thus may be removed a general deluge or any great catastrophe'.

Chapter 8e

HUTTON'S CHAPTER V OF VOLUME I 'CONCERNING THAT WHICH MAY BE TERMED THE PRIMARY PART OF THE PRESENT EARTH'

'Alternations of Land and Water'

The various mineral causes, Hutton thinks, are cyclic in their nature, though with different periods. 'The succession of light and darkness is that which, in those operations, appears to us most steady'; that 'of heat and cold comes next'; while 'the succession of wet and dry . . . is often to us irregular.'

Let us here consider alternations of land and water. Upheaval of continents made of indurated marine sediments indicates, we are told, 'expansion of matter, placed below that land. . . . It is here not inquired by what mechanism this separation is to be performed;' but it is clear that the support thus provided may eventually fail, leading to resubmersion. This in turn allows of fresh collection of sediment, with subsequent reconsolidation and upheaval. In such case, what remains of the old continent 'must have undergone a double course of mineral changes and displacement; consequently, the effect of subterranean heat or fusion must be more apparent in this mass, and the marks of its original formation more and more obliterated. . . . If this conclusion shall be thought to be reasonable, then here is an explanation of the alpine schistus masses of our land, those parts which have been erroneously considered primitive in the constitution of the earth'. As pointed out presently (p. 82), Hutton's Chapter V was written in its present form before its author had seen *exposed* unconformities in Arran, the Jed and Siccar Point, 1787–1788.

1779 *De Luc disowns the Term Primitive*

Hutton quotes freely from de Luc's published letters to show how complexities of foliation eventually led this philosopher to question his own previous recognition of stratification among crystalline schists. By 1779 de Luc adopted a two-fold grouping of rocks in general: *Primordial* (unfossiliferous and of unknown origin) and *Secondary* (fossiliferous and of marine origin). In this classification de Luc substituted Primordial for Primitive, because the latter had come to be associated with the idea of deposition in a primitive ocean, regarding which he now wanted to adopt an obviously non-committed attitude.

Hutton for his part, in the 1788 edition of his *Theory,* introduced *Primary* in place of *Primitive,* but for a different reason. His Primaries were the oldest rocks of his experience, but not the oldest in the long history of the earth, which for him showed 'no vestige of a beginning'.

De Luc in the Harz Mountains

Hutton passes on to quote from de Luc's letters an account of a traverse he had made in the Harz Mountains. We need not delay over what the two have to say regarding mineral veins cutting Primordial schist capped by Secondary limestone. There is considerable agreement, which may be gathered from the following statement by de Luc: 'I have always been inclined to attribute them [the veins] in part to the operations of subterranean fires'.

Another interesting topic which de Luc mentions is a surprising dispersal of granite boulders from a prolongation of the Brocken. In explanation he invokes a tremendous explosion. Hutton, on the other hand, suggests a comparison with the dispersal of granite boulders round Mt. Blanc (p. 104, 107, 111), where, he thinks, greatly extended glaciers of the past served as distributors.

1778, 1779 *Discordances of Two Kinds*

We may now turn to two discordances presented in reverse order: 1779 in the Harz and 1778 in the Glarus Alps.

In the Harz example (1779) secondary limestone rests flat, and to all appearances undisturbed, on schist which, as so often, shows contorted layering. De Luc admittedly did not know what had caused this contortion (p. 80), but he clearly realised that it had not been developed during the upheaval of the overlying limestone, which shows no sign of trouble within its own substance. From this he draws the unwarranted conclusion that the limestone has never moved up or down after its deposition in the sea. Instead of upheaval of the limestone, he postulates a great withdrawal of the sea. He admits that he had seen at other localities obvious disturbance of the limestone; but, in view of this particular exposure, he attributed such happenings to mere local accidents. Hutton points out that 'this philosopher will acknowledge, that those natural appearances, on any particular place, will be the same, whether we suppose the bottom of the sea to have been raised, . . . or the surface of the sea to have sunk'. He then gives his own interpretation: 'If, therefore, strata had been deposited upon broken and bare rocks of schistus, it is probably that these had been sunk in the sea after having been exposed to the atmosphere, and served the purpose of land upon the globe'. In other words, Hutton thinks that de Luc had seen, without knowing it, an *exposed unconformity;* and he goes on to cite supporting evidence supplied by fragments of schist contained in a sandstone seen elsewhere by de Luc overlying the limestone.

We may recall what we have already said on pp. 51, 80, and what Tomkeieff had previously emphasised (1962, p. 395), namely, that Hutton's Chapter V, though unpublished till 1795, was written before his discovery of exposed unconformities in Arran, Jedburgh and Siccar Point, 1787–1788. We may quote again what Hutton says on the subject at the close of his Chapter V:

'Since writing this chapter, I am enabled to speak more devisively upon that point [exposed unconformity], having acquired more light upon the subject, as will appear in the next chapter.'

Meanwhile, let us consider the second instance of discordance, which Hutton quotes from de Luc, 1778. By chance it concerns, not a stratigraphical unconformity, but what might well be described as a structural unconformity. It owes its main characters, not to erosion and deposition, but to overthrusting and folding. This introduces a dramatic element into the story, for the Glarus overthrust is the most famous of its kind in the whole world. Its description in 1841 by Escher von der Linth marks the recognition of large-scale tectonics in the structure of the Alps and various other mountain chains. De Luc's account reads as follows:

'The district is very unusual in its lithogeognosy. It is rare elsewhere to find so many interesting phenomena gathered together in a single locality, and so various an association of structures. It is the place in Switzerland most deserving of examination; and it is the most difficult to understand that we have encountered. One must remember that we have mounted all the way from Glarus, and now we stand at the foot of these astonishing peaks that dominate the high Alps. One finds here an unwonted possibility to examine the foundations of these colossi which crown the globe. As a rule such foundations are hidden by debris and landslips. Here is a bluish schist, hard and compact and traversed by veins of white and yellow quartz. In it a path has been cut to allow of passage on foot. This rock rises to a prodigeous height nearly vertical with beds* dipping at 80°. One's imagination is terrified at seeing that such masses have been loosened and displaced to the extent of having made nearly a quarter of a complete revolution. After climbing up and following this rock among stones and scree for an hour and a half, one finds the schist surmounted by limestone lying at a great height with horizontal bedding. The schist immediately below the limestone has the same

* Written shortly before de Luc had adopted an agnostic position regarding the layering of Primitive, later called Primordial, rocks (see p. 80).

steep dip as at the foot of the hills'.

Hutton admits that this account certainly suggests that de Luc is right in supposing 'that strata had been deposited upon those *schisti* after they had been changed from their natural or horizontal position, and become vertical; 'at the same time', he continues, 'this conclusion is not a necessary consequence, without examining concomitant appearances, and finding particular marks by which this operation might be traced; for the simply finding horizontal strata placed above vertical or much inclined schist, is not sufficient, of itself, to constitute that fact, while it is acknowledged that every species of fracture, dislocation, and contortion, is to be found among the displaced strata of the globe.'

One can truly say that Hutton, in 1795, foresaw the possibility, which Escher, in 1841, proved with the help of fossils. The upturned bluish schist is now known to be Tertiary. The overlying horizontal limestone is Jurassic; and above it lies a great mass of Permian, Trias, etc.

Chapter 8*f*

HUTTON'S CHAPTER VI OF VOLUME I 'THEORY OF INTERCHANGING SEA AND LAND ILLUSTRATED BY AN INVESTIGATION OF THE PRIMARY AND SECONDARY STRATA'

1787 *'Section i. A Distinct View of the Primary and Secondary Strata'*

Hutton reminds us that the Southern Uplands of Scotland, separating low-lying country to north and south, are made of Primary strata of marine origin. He cites *attitude* as the most persistent distinction between Primaries and Secondaries in this area: the former stand more or less vertical; and the latter more or less horizontal. Also, it is a very general rule that the Primaries are more consolidated than the Secondaries. He had, therefore, before going to Arran, searched without success for actual exposures of the Primary–Secondary contact. At the same time, on approaching a hidden contact, he 'frequently found a confused mass, formed of the fragments of those Alpine [Primary] Strata mixed with materials of the horizontal Secondary bodies'. This raised a question which troubled him considerably: Were these breccias of sedimentary or tectonic origin? Were they, in fact, true breccia-conglomerates, or false crush-conglomerates?

At last in Arran, 1787, he found near Loch Ranza a clear exposure of Highland schist (Primary) in contact with Old Red Sandstone (Secondary). Both formations dip fairly steeply, but in opposite directions, giving a junction of T type; and the bedding of the Old Red Sandstone truncates that of the schist; but there is no development of anything like a basal conglomerate, so that Hutton's particular problem remained unsolved.

By good fortune, however, in the same year, 1787, he found what he sought on the banks of the River Jed: a thin breccia-conglomerate separating vertical Silurian (Primary) from overlying horizontal Old Red Sandstone (Secondary). Hutton examined the evidence carefully, and decided that appearances almost certainly showed that the conglomerate had been produced by subaerial or coastal erosion of uptilted Primary, and that its accumulation marked the beginning of a fresh period of subsidence. Hutton also felt it was safe to interpret in the same fashion all the marginal breccias he had found elsewhere in the Uplands. There is so much good sense in this interpretation, that we may forgive his assumption that the Secondary formation at Jedburgh is marine—it is actually continental Old Red Sandstone. Also we need not take too seriously his exaggeration of the part heat has played in the consolidation of the strata concerned.

After Jedburgh, Hutton found in Teviotdale another exposure of the unconformity separating Southern Upland Primaries from conglomeratic Old Red Sandstone Secondaries. He wrote an account of this for publication in his book to be; and then read in the *Esprit de Journeaux* an abstract of a memoir by Johann Karl Wilhelm Voigt describing a very similar state of affairs in Germany. Voigt (1752–1821) was a distinguished pupil of Werner, who afterwards turned against his master. The memoir cited deals with Thuringia, where so-called Primitive schist is widely overlain by Secondaries; and where the basal bed of the latter has long been called by local miners the *sol mort rouge—sol,* because of its position as the sole of the Secondaries; *mort,* because infertile from the mineral point of view; and *rouge,* because of the frequent red colour of its matrix. 'This bed is composed of a prodigeous quantity of rounded stones, bound together by red and even grey argillaceous material, the whole rendered rather hard'. The boulders and pebbles found in the *sol mort rouge* can be matched in every case with rocks in neighbouring 'Primitive'.

'Here', says Hutton, 'we find the same observations in the mountains of Germany that I have been making with regard to those of Scotland'. He does not intend in this sentence to institute a close correlation as regards date. We now know that the basal Secondaries in Scotland are of Old Red Sandstone age, and in Thuringia of New Red Sandstone age; but this is a refinement that could not have been foreseen in Hutton's day.

1788 *'Section ii. The Theory Confirmed from Observations made on Purpose to Elucidate the Subject'*

Hutton recounts how he got a friend to explore what may be called the Dunglass region of East Lothian and Berwickshire in anticipation of a visit by himself and Playfair to Sir James Hall. This preliminary exploration resulted in the discovery of additional exposures of the Jedburgh–Teviotdale unconformity near Dunglass in the Tour and Pease Burns.

Hutton and Playfair arrived, as planned, early in June, 1788, and were blessed with good weather. They first checked, along with their host, the reported exposures in the Tour and Pease Burns. 'The schistose strata here approach towards the vertical; and the sandstone is greatly inclined. . . . Here again, though we have not a regular pudding-stone, we have that which corresponds to it, as having been the effect of similar circumstances. These are the fracture and detritus of the schistus, while the strata were deposited upon the broken ends of the schistus at the bottom of the sea. Most of the fragments of the schistus have their angles sharp; consequently, they had not travelled far, or been much worn by attrition. But more or less does not alter the nature of an operation, and the pudding-stone, which at Jedburgh is interposed between the vertical schistus and the horizontal strata, is here properly represented by the included fragments of the schistus in the inclined strata'.

We have already quoted (p. 56) somewhat fully Playfair's account of the impressions which overwhelmed him when the party, on a subsequent day, sailed along the coast and landed for a time at Siccar Point. We need not, therefore, enlarge upon Hutton's more restrained statement that 'the sandstone strata are partly washed away, and partly remaining upon the ends of the vertical schistus'.

When they re-embarked to travel towards St. Abbs, the party were surprised to see abundant ripple-marks on successive beds of the schist. They were also delighted by a number of folds affecting the schists; and Hutton reproduces a sketch by Hall figuring good examples associated with a minute horizontal 'shift or hitch'.

To follow up the results of this momentous voyage, the three friends made their way up one of the tributaries of the Dunglass Burn. They sought a further exposure of the unconformity, but found instead what made the latter 'sufficiently evident, and was at the same time an object far more interesting in our eyes'—Hutton probably spoke for himself alone in this sentence. Voigt's description, from which we have quoted above, tells how the *sol mort rouge* 'in places forms entire mountains; here', says Hutton, 'we have a perfect example of the same thing; and, the moment we saw it, we said, here is the *sol mort rouge*. . . . What we had hitherto seen of this pudding-stone was but a few fragments of the schistus in the lower beds of the sandstone; here a mountain of water-worn schisti, embedded in a red earth and consolidated, presented itself to our view. . . . Upon the coast we have but a specimen of the pudding-stone; most of the fragments had their angles entire; and few of them are rounded by attrition. But the difference is only in degree, and not in kind; the stones are the same, and the nature of the composition similar'. All this is true. The imposing mass of conglomerate at which they looked is now known to be the infilling of an ancient valley which later geologists have traced across the Uplands.

Chapter 8g

HUTTON'S CHAPTER VII OF VOLUME I 'OPINIONS EXAMINED WITH REGARD TO PETRIFACTION OR MINERAL CONCRETION'

Hutton in much of his Chapter VII is at his worst. He bitterly attacks a number of his fellow naturalists for not accepting his theory of consolidation by partial fusion. One feels that he protests too much. His object, he assures us, is 'to show that what has been wrote by naturalists, upon this subject, has only a tendency to corrupt science, by admitting the grossest supposition in place of fact'.

Buffon's ideas concerning the regularities of crystallisation he dismisses as 'plainly inconceivable'; whereas a more generous critic might see in them a serviceable beginning.

De Luc, he tells us, in this theory of Petrifaction sets out with the acknowledged principle of cohesion, and, in order to consolidate strata of a porous texture, he supposes water carrying minute bodies of all shapes and sizes and depositing them in such close contact as to produce solidity and concretion by attraction. 'But how', Hutton asks, 'apply this principle to consolidation?—only by supposing all the separate bodies, of which the solid is to be composed, to be in perfect contact in all their surfaces'.

De Luc, turning from physics to chemistry, has also tried to illustrate natural consolidation of strata by analogy with the artificial consolidation of the materials of a wall with the help of mortar. Hutton admits that either of de Luc's suggested means of consolidation, physical or chemical, might perhaps operate successfully, if only one could introduce the proper constituents from outside, and persuade them to deposit interstitial material in solid form; but this could not happen in the stagnant waters of the deep sea bottom, where alone, he claimed, consolidation occurs on a significant scale—surely as a result of heating under pressure.

Obviously too de Luc's chemical consolidation requires that the cement involved can be dissolved in water under appropriate conditions. Let us first consider *siliceous cement:* 'To alledge the possibility of water being capable of disolving those bodies in the mineral regions, and of thus changing the substance of one body into another . . . is so far from tending to increase our science, that it is abandoning the human intellect to be bewildered in an error; it is the vain attempt of lulling to sleep the scientific conscience and making the soul of man insensible to the natural distress of conscious ignorance'.

It is amazing to read the above and then to hear Hutton quietly saying: 'Although siliceous substance is not soluble, in so far as we know, by simple water, it is soluble by means of alkali substance [our p. 37]; consequently, it is possible it may be dissolved in the earth'. And again: 'We have another substance for the dissolution of siliceous substance. This is the fluor acid which volatilises the siliceous substance'—hydrofluoric acid had been obtained by C. Scheele in 1771 by the action of sulphuric acid on fluor spar. As regards the alkaline solution of siliceous matter, he admits: 'Without knowing the principle upon which it proceeds, we here perceive a natural operation by which siliceous petrifaction may be performed'; but he seems to think this type of petrifaction too rare to influence his theories.

'The concretion of calcareous matter upon the surface of the earth is perhaps the only example upon which [the Neptunists] theory is founded'. Here, *above* the level of the sea, the general tendency is to waste the calcareous bodies through which water percolates; and, Hutton points out, this is only locally compensated by depostion of stalactitic. Such precipitation of stalactitic matter cannot be expected to continue *below* the level of the sea; and the same holds good for 'many other mineral bodies which are decomposed and dissolved upon the surface of the earth'. Even if there were general petrifaction 'above the level of the sea, where there might be a circulation of air and a percolation of water. How could the strata of the earth below the level of the sea be petrified?'

Though Hutton had always found, to his own satisfaction, that consolidation of marine sediments had clearly resulted from the fluid state of fusion, he was now prepared to contemplate a variant. In it infiltration co-operates with heating, very much in geyser fashion (though he does not say so). When the temperature is high, solvent may be expelled from interstices as steam, leaving behind a precipitate. When again the temperature falls, a fresh supply of solution may filter in.

Hutton now quotes at length from an account by de Carosi, who, in 1783, studied in Poland 'metamorphism' of pure and impure limestone into flint with quartz. Carosi concluded that the first process was to saturate the limestone with dilute acid—for instance, dilute sulphuric acid derived from pyrites—which could remove the calcareous earth in solution as gypsum, at the same time opening up interstices through liberation of fixed air (CO_2). 'But', says Hutton, 'even supposing that such a process were to be exhibited, still it would remain to be explained, how this process, which requires conditions certainly not found at the bottom of the sea, could be accomplished in that place, where the strata of the earth had been deposited, accumulated, consolidated, and metamorphosed'.

It is interesting to find both de Carosi and Hutton employing the term *metamorphosis,* since its introduction into geological literature is generally ascribed to Lyell. Presumably Lyell standardised its employment by omitting the results of low-temperature reactions now commonly ascribed to diagenesis.

Hutton also quotes extensively from de Carosi's detailed description of flintification of sandstone—always sandstone with calcareous cement. Hutton does 'not pretend to understand the manner of operating' flintification as proposed by de Carosi. On the other hand, he 'maintains that here, as everywhere in general, the loose incoherent strata of the globe have been petrified, that is, consolidated, by the fusion of their substances'.

As for Cronstedt's amygdaloids, 'the Chevalier de Dolomieu supposes these rocks to have been erupted lavas', and their amygdales to be the infillings of vesicles; whereas de Carossi, 'on the contrary, supposes these formed by a species of chymical transmutation of calcareous and argillaceous earths, which, if not altogether incomprehensible, is at least not in any degree, so far as I know, a thing to be understood. . . . Petrifaction is a subject in which mineralogists have perhaps wandered more widely from the truth than in any other part of natural history; and the reason is plain. The mineral operations of nature lie in a part of the globe which is necessarily inaccessable to man'.

We are then told how Patrin, in the *Journal de Physique* for 1791, says that 'all who visit the interior of the earth know that even the most compact of rocks are intimately penetrated by humidity; and the fluid concerned is certainly not pure water; this is the agent which directs all the operations, all the crystallisations, all the works of nature in the mineral kingdom. Hence one can easily conceive that, thanks to this fluid, a circulation reigns in the most intimate part of subterranean bodies; and that this continually transports the chemical elements until through the force of their affinities corpuscles of similar kind take the form which nature has assigned to them'.

Hutton's reaction to all this is emphatic. 'It is,' he says, 'to reason fantastically, and to imagine fable'.

From Patrin, Hutton turns to A. G. Monnet, best known for his completion, in 1780, of a mineralogical map of France and England, initiated by Guettard. Hutton quotes extensively from an account of slate published by Monnet in the *Journal de Physique* for 1784. In this, Monnet follows Guettard in explaining the apparent disappearance of water of solution in the process which leads to the development of, say, quartz. According to them, there is no need to look for cavities or channels, to accommodate or conduct away water released during the crystallisation of quartz. There has been no separation of substance, only joint solidification of silica and water. Accordingly 'this general fluid [water] may be the element of the solid bodies of the mineral kingdom, as it is of the solid bodies of the vegetable and animal kingdoms.' Monnet illustrates this theory by reference to impressive growths of quartz in a pure limestone exposed at Champigny on the outskirts of Paris.

Hutton welcomes Monnet's recognition of the disappearance problem, as it may be called; but points out that he has substituted for it 'a mere supposition, viz., that nature may have the power of converting water, in those secret places, into some other thing'. One feels, however, that Monnet's suggestion was not altogether absurd at the time it was made. We must remember the uncertainty that attaches to water in flint and some of the zeolites, not to mention the obvious importance of water of crystallization in many well known salts. It was, however, a supposition that could not stand up to laboratory examination.

We here reach a good part of Hutton's Chapter VII, which deals with the solubility of silica in alkali water, and with its deposition as sinter in the geyser basins of Iceland. Hutton introduces the subject very frankly. The naturalists who oppose him have, he says, 'something apparently in their favour, which it may be proper now to mention'.

We need not repeat what we have already said (pp. 37, 87) upon the hearing of the Icelandic phenomenon on the general theory of consolidation. Rather, let us notice a few circumstances of historic interest, remembering all the time that Robert Wilhelm von Bunsen did not make his famous visit until 1846.

We have told (p. 43) how Sir Joseph Banks set out in 1772 to investigate some of the wonders of Iceland, and how on his way he 'discovered' Staffa. Returning, Hutton tells us, he brought back to Scotland, 'specimens of the petrifactions of the Giezer. Dr Black and I [Hutton] first discovered that these were of a siliceous substance. I have always conjectured that the water of Giezer must be impregnated with flinty matter by means of an alkaline substance, and so expressed my opinion in the *Theory of the Earth* published in the Transactions of the Royal Society of Edinburgh. We have therefore been very desirous of procuring some of that water, in order to have it analysed.

'An opportunity favourable to our views has occurred this summer. Mr Stanley set out from this place with the same purpose of examining Iceland. He was good enough to ask Dr Black and I what inquiries we would incline that he should make. We have now, by the favour of this gentleman, obtained specimens of the petrifaction of Giezer; and what is still more interesting, we have procured some of the water of those petrifying boiling springs.

'It appears from these specimens, that the boiling water which is ejected from those aqueous volcanoes, if we may use the expression, is endued with the quality of forming two different species of petrifaction or incrustation, for, besides the siliceous bodies, of which we had before received specimens, the same stream of water incrustates its channel with a calcareous substance. All the specimens which I have seen consist of incrustation, some purely siliceous, some calcareous, and others mixed of those two, more or less.

'Dr Black has been analysing the water, and he finds in it siliceous matter dissolved in the alkaline substance in the manner of liquor silicum. My conjecture has thus been verified'.

Chapter 8*h*

HUTTON'S CHAPTER VIII OF VOLUME I 'THE NATURE OF MINERAL COAL, AND THE FORMATION OF BITUMINOUS STRATA, INVESTIGATED'

'Section i—Purpose of this Inquiry'

Hutton refers back to joints as affording a 'perfect mark' by which to decide whether consolidation of strata has been effected by water alone or by heat. The joints, according to him, have arisen 'from the contraction of the mass, distended by heat, and contracted in cooling'. Most mineralogists have failed to understand. 'They have explained mineralogy by infiltration. . . . How shall we inform such observators; How reason with those who attend not to an argument!'

Hutton decides to repeat in Sections ii and iii the independent evidence of subterranean heat which mineral coal affords through the distillation of its volatile components—his wording is very obscure hereabouts.

Before proceeding further in this line, Hutton switches to another indication of heating, which, he thinks, coal-bearing strata show in abundance. He finds in coal seams and in veins that traverse them, large masses and isolated crystals of pyrites. This he wrongly regards as evidence of a high temperature, for water and air acting at ordinary temperatures tend to decompose pyrites, not produce to it.

Section ii—Natural History of Coal Strata, and Theory of their Geological Operation

Hutton was a confirmed driftist in his theory of coal formation. For him, all consolidated strata have collected as loose material upon the bottom of the deep sea; and this assumption of his included coal along with its associates.

It was the alteration, not the formation, of coal strata, which specially interested him. In this matter 'the varieties of coal are distinguished by their different manner of burning. . . . Thus we have one species of coal [bituminous] which is extremely fusible, abounds with oil, and consequently is inflammable; we have another again [anthracite] which is perfectly fixed and infusible in the fire'.

Hutton argues that the bituminous variety is nearer the original material than the anthracite variety, for one can alter bituminous coal by heating it to coke—and coke has 'every essential quality', though not 'precisely the exterior appearance' of natural anthracite; on the other hand, 'it is not in the nature of things to change the infusible species, so as to make it fusible or oily.'

Hutton next returns to consider the nature of coal sediment before it is consolidated to mineral coal. The burnable part of coal he considered to be plant and animal material derived, partly from the continents, partly from the ocean. The unburnable part, that is the ash left on combustion, he regarded as inorganic earth. The burnable part had three possible sources: (1) volatile effluent from maturing coal seams; (2) combustion of life products on the surface of the earth; and (3) river-borne humic products from peat mosses and forests. He made no attempt to allocate relative importance to these three sources.

Coal showed to his pocket lens no visible indication of being a mixture of substances; so he considered that both its organic and inorganic materials must have been reduced to impalpable dust before settling on the bottom of the sea.

Here Hutton departs from the main subject, to give an interesting account of a particular minor type of mineral coal 'called Kennel coal [often spelt Cannel] in England, and in Scotland Parrot coal'. It has so little appearance of bedding that it may require an expert to recognise its stratification. If, however, such an expert lights a surface broken across the bedding, the coal burns quietly, like a candle. If on the other hand he ignites a bedding surface, the coal burns with 'violent cracking and explosions' reminiscent of a noisy parrot. The contrast is due to the ease with which volatiles can pass along the bedding, as compared with the difficulty they find in escaping across the same.

Returning to the main subject, Hutton points out that 'the strata that attend coal, . . . commonly, almost universally, abound with the most distinct evidence of vegetable substances. . . . There is much fossil coal, particularly that termed in England clod coal, . . . that shows abundance of vegetable bodies. . . . Fossil wood in strata, for example the Bovey coal in Devonshire, . . . is in appearance undistinguishable from fossil coal, and may be also in great quantity. . . . Thus the strata of fossil coal would appear to be formed by the subsidence of inflammable matter of every species at the bottom of the sea, in places distant from the shore, or where there had been much repose, and where the lightest and most floatant bodies have been deposited together'; while interstratification of coal and other sediments can easily be accounted for by assuming variations in the direction and force of oceanic currents.

Structural Considerations

Hutton now turns to the disturbances so clearly traceable in mines. Here we are very fortunate in having a wonderful account, brought to light by David Tait, of what was already known, a hundred years before Hutton's day, concerning the geometry of the Mid Lothian coal field, just east of Edinburgh. This information is conveyed in a special part of a book on hydrostatics, 1672, written by George Sinclar, who for 20 years was Professor of Philosophy and Mathematics in the University of Glasgow. Sinclar's tenure of academic office was discontinuous, for, having a distaste for bishops, he was expelled in 1666, and did not return till 1688. His period of exile he largely spent as a mining engineer in the Lothians; and, it was while thus employed, he produced his *Hydrostatics* with its *Short History of Coal, and of all the Common, and Proper Accidents thereof; a Subject never treated of Before.*

It will convince anyone of the continuity of geological thought to find Sinclar using the words 'cropp', 'rise' and 'streek', with the same meaning, though not with the same spelling, as holds good today. Moreover, he employs the terms 'gae', 'dyke' or 'trouble', just as Scots miners still do, to cover *both* the dykes and the *faults* of modern text-books.

Here we may interpolate that neither Sinclar nor Hutton seems ever to have used the word fault. Playfair in his *Illustrations,* 1802, does indeed employ the term at least once; but he accompanies it with an explanation, as though Scottish readers were not likely to be familar with it already. Thus we read that recent tunnelling operations in Yorkshire, reported in the *Philosophical Transactions,* have exposed 'what is called a fault, throw or break, or what we have here called a shift'.

Furthermore, Sinclar cites the experience of the coal-hewers that the side on which the coal will be found to be 'down'. As regards 'dipp', he agrees with those who contend that 'dipp', unless interrupted by a 'gae', continues to a centre, where the coal, or whatever it may be, 'takes a contrary course' which brings it up once again to the 'grass'. This proposition he applies to the Mid Lothian basin, boldly accepting a hypothesis that carries him in imagination 3,000 ft. below the limit of his experience. What appealed to him was the fact that he could follow the outcrop of the Great Seam, fairly satisfactorily, round the margin of the basin, generally with inward dip. He knew this particular seam in its various exposures by its character, by the rocks lying above, and by the neighbouring coals below. He also speaks of many other coals lying well above the great seam in the heart of the basin. A notable beginning had been made in deciphering Scottish Carboniferous stratigraphy.

Apart from the geometrical side of his subject, Sinclar seems to have made but little headway with the study of the rocks. As a geologist he cannot compare, for instance, with his predecessor Leonardo da Vinci, or his contemporaries Nikolaus Steno or Robert

Hooke. He makes no mention of fossils; and, when he says that coal near a 'gae' or whin-rock is rendered 'as if it were already burnt', he is merely summarising common experience—he is not propounding a geological theorem.

Hutton was probably acquainted with Sinclar's views, either directly or through his friends the Clerks; but his outlook on the geometry of a coalfield was rather different. Instead of seeking guidance for the planning of mines, Hutton was happy in matching the various attitudes of coal seams with what he saw in every other kind of stratum which he examined. The only difference he found was that the structural phenomena are 'much better known in those of coal, by having, from their great utility in the arts of life, become a subject for mining and thus been traced in the earth at great expense, and for a long extent'.

The Mid Lothian coals are exceptional in that along the north-west margin of the field they stand 'in an erect posture, even almost perpendicular to the plane in which they had been formed'. In this position the miners call them 'edge seams'. In other parts of the field the coals are almost or quite flat. 'Thus, it will appear, that every possible change from the original position of those strata may have happened, and are daily found from our experience in those mines'.

Hutton, of course, attributed all these complications to earth movement resulting in general, but diversified, upheaval. He then discusses in the same context the miners' term 'trouble'. Apparently he found that it was applied to any structural irregularity that tended to upset mining practice. Thus a change of dip was a *trouble,* and also what we call a fault—a plane where a coal breaks off abruptly with manifest displacement. 'This', he says, 'is by miners termed a *slip, hitch,* or *dyke.*'

'These irregularities', he continues, 'may either be attended with an injected body of subterraneous lava or basaltes, here termed whin-stone, or they may not be attended, at least apparently'—by which he means that absence of whin may perhaps be only local.

Hutton then passes on to divide Scotland very roughly into regions of Alpine or Primary rocks and regions of flat or secondary rocks, the latter pierced by numerous intrusions of whin. He notes that he has found no coal in the Primary regions, which, unless it can be explained away, contradicts his exaggerated ideas of repetitive uniformity in nature. Nothing daunted, however, he suggests that coal seams were originally present in the Primaries, but have been burnt out during subsequent metamorphism; and he recalls a coal in supposed Primaries at Mat in Switzerland. One feels that this suggestion was good, though entirely mistaken.

The rest of Section ii of Hutton's Chapter viii contains very little that has not been said earlier in his book. We may, however, close by quoting a paragraph in which the importance of erosion in shaping the face of Scotland is given due prominence:

'If we shall thus allow the principle of consolidation, consequently also of induration, to have been much exerted upon the strata of the alpine country, and but moderately or little upon those of the *low* country of Scotland, we shall evidently see one reason, perhaps the only one, for the lesser elevation of the one country above the level of the sea, than the other. This is because the one resists the powers that have been employed in levelling what has been raised from the bottom of the sea, more than the other; consequently we find more of the one remaining above the level of the sea than of the other'.

'Section iii—The Mineralogical Operations of the Earth illustrated from the Theory of Fossil Coal'

Hutton, with fair success, once again presents his theory of natural distillation of coaly matter in terms of phlogistic chemistry. Every plant and animal, he says, contains volatile inflammable and non-volatile combustible substances, and these are always united together, never separate. The chymical principle of the one is the hydrogenous principle, or that of inflammable air'; and of the other, 'proper carbonic matter', such as abounds in coke or blind coal (anthracite). The artificial separation of these two principles, both of which contain phlogiston or 'fixed light' derived through plants from the sun, always requires heat. When common coal is 'completely distilled, it becomes a perfect coal of a porous or spongy texture. Such a substance is extremely rare among minerals; I [Hutton] have however found it. It is in the harbour of Ayr, where a whinstone dyke traverses the coal strata, and includes some of that substance in the state of coaks or cinder. I pointed this out many years ago to Dr Black; and lately I showed it to Professor Playfair.

'But the culm of South Wales, the Kilkenny coal of Ireland, and the blind coal of Scotland, not withstanding that these are a perfect coal, have nothing of the porous construction of the specimen which I have just mentioned; they are perfectly solid, and break with a smooth shining surface like those which emit smoke and flame.

'Here is therefore a mineral operation in the preparation of those coals which we cannot imitate'.

Strangely enough Hutton offers no explicit explanation of the lack of spongy textures in blind coals. He merely says that 'the operation of heat' must have been 'under the proper circumstances for distillation or evaporation'.

Hutton then refers to occasional occurrences of plumbago, or something very like it—two from abroad, others from Ayrshire and Cumberland. He argues that the minerals concerned have had their 'origin in vegetable substance' and that they have been brought to their present state 'by the operation of mineral fire or heat, . . . although we are ignorant of the circumstances by which their differences [from blind coal] and their peculiar chymical and mechanical properties have been produced'. He does not suggest that the special circumstances may include unusually high temperature; but then he was aware that some of the carbon of man-made coke is in the form of plumbago.

Here we come to the end of Hutton's Volume I. Its closing words remind us of its initial paragraph, for we read:

'We shall thus be led to admire the wisdom of nature, providing for the continuation of this living world, and employing those very means by which, in a more partial view of things, this beautiful structure of an inhabited earth seems to be necessarily going into destruction.'

'END OF VOLUME FIRST'

Chapter 9

1795
HUTTON'S THEORY OF THE EARTH IN BOOK FORM 'WITH PROOFS AND ILLUSTRATIONS' VOLUME II

'FARTHER INDUCTION OF FACTS AND OBSERVATIONS, RESPECTING THE GEOLOGICAL PART OF THE THEORY'

Hutton's *Introduction* tells us that the emergent land can have no provision for river courses. Drainage valleys must therefore have been river-made. Joint operation of three causes must have determined the form of the land. These are:

(1) Regular stratification on the sea bottom of the materials that are later to make land.

(2) Deep-seated operations causing effects, some regular, others irregular. Among the former we may include contraction joints.

(3) Superficial operations due to sun and atmosphere, wind and water, rivers and tides.

Chapter 9*a*

HUTTON'S CHAPTER I OF HIS VOLUME II 'FACTS IN CONFIRMATION OF THE THEORY OF ELEVATING THE LAND ABOVE THE SURFACE OF THE SEA'

Let us, says Hutton, examine beds for 'that change of posture and of shape which is so frequently found in mountainous countries, among the strata that had been originally almost plain and horizontal. Here it is also that an opportunity is presented of having sections of these objects, by which the internal construction of the earth is to be known. It is our business to lay before the reader examples of this kind, examples which are clearly described, and which may be examined at pleasure.

'No person has had better opportunities of examining the structure of mountains than M. de Saussure, and nobody more capable of examining those comprehensive views that are so necessary for the proper execution of such a task'.

A complication here obtrudes itself: de Saussure changed his mind at least twice on the question as to whether steep dips denote subsequent disturbance, or, instead, are original features of mountain-making beds. The significant dates are 1774, 1779 and 1786.

In 1774 de Saussure looked out with inspiration from viewpoints in the western Alps (Gramont, see p. 102). 'I saw', says he, 'that the shadowy connexions that I had already observed in relation to the material of the primitives and secondaries, extended also the the form and situation of these beds. . . . I concluded from these two connexions, that, since the secondary mountains had been formed in the bosom of the waters, the primitives also had this origin. I saw their materials arrange themselves horizontally in concentric beds; and then fire, or some other elastic fluids enclosed in the interior of the globe, raised and punctured the skin, thus forcing out some of the primitive interior'. All this was in fair agreement with Hutton, whose first publication on the subject was in his paper presented to the Edinburgh R.S. in 1785.

In 1779 de Saussure published Volume I of his *Voyage dans les Alpes,* and withdrew from some of his 1774 anticipations. This mattered little to Hutton, who read authors for their observations, rather than their interpretations. Thus he had no doubt that de Saussure was right in still saying that he had found similar roof-like structures in 'several secondary mountains, both in the Alps and elsewhere, and above all in a great number of primitive mountains'. On the other hand, Hutton disagreed with de Saussure when the latter gave up his original idea that the steep dips in the Jura mountains had resulted from tilting during 'some revolution'. De Saussure's change of interpretation in this case came from his meeting steep beds 'in well preserved mountains . . . and his perceiving an unexpectedly great regularity in their form and direction'. His conclusion was 'that nature could quite well form some beds in a very inclined position, even perpendicular'. Turning next to the frontal Alps, de Saussure again finds great apparent deformation, but asks: 'What is the force which has been able to give these beds their present situation? . . . I should be pained to have recourse to these almost supernatural agencies, especially as I have found no vestige at all of their presence . . . no trace of fire'. De Saussure then passes on to other extreme examples in the Alps: 'These divers beds are so easily followed in all their shapes; and so strangely interlaced that I can scarcely believe that they have been formed in a horizontal position, and that later disturbances have given them their present bizzare attitudes. It would be necessary to suppose that these disturbances occurred when the beds were soft and perfectly flexible, for one sees in them no sign of rupture. . . . No, in my opinion, only crystallisation can render intelligible these fantastic forms. Accordingly, I should not revolt against the idea that the rock of the cascade [a difficult case discussed in his text] has in fact been able to form in the position in which it is at present'. Hutton in his criticism allows that stalactitic layering does 'give an appearance of stratification', but it is 'to a figure which is absolutely inconsistent with stratification, an operation which is performed by depositing materials at the bottom of the sea'.

In 1786 de Saussure published Volume II of his *Voyages,* in which he accepted vertical beds as undoubtedly a result of subsequent deformation. He owed his reconversion to finding a thick conglomerate at Valorsine. Attracted by loose blocks of the conglomerate, de Saussure climbed uphill to examine exposures in place. His feelings on arrival are thus recorded: 'Just imagine my astonishment at finding the beds vertical. One will easily understand the cause of this astonishment when one realises that it is impossible for these conglomerates to have been deposited in this situation. That particles of extreme tenuity, suspended in a liquid can be agglutinated among themselves to form vertical beds is proved by what we see in alabaster and agates, and even in artificial crystallisations; but that a fully formed stone of the size of a man's head can stand still in the middle of a vertical layer until the little particles of the rock come along, enveloping, soldering and fixing it in this position is an absurd and impossible supposition. It must be recognised as demonstrated that these conglomerates were formed in a nearly horizontal position and then upheaved after consolidation. What is the cause of their upheaval, we still do not know; but it is an important step forward to realise that, among the prodigeous number of vertical beds which we meet in the Alps, some without any doubt started their existence in a horizontal position.' 'Here', comments Hutton, 'M. de Saussure, who is always more anxious to establish truth, than preserve theory, gives up the formation of the Alpine strata by crystallisation'.

Hutton's main object now is to show that de Saussure's descriptions call for the operation of fire, though their author firmly disagrees. Thus we find Hutton closing his Chapter 1 with the following words: 'I flatter myself, that when he [de Saussure] shall have considered the arguments which have been employed for the manifold, the general operations of subterranean fire, as well as for the long continued operations of water on the surface of the erected land, he will not seek any other operation'.

Vain aspiration! Time was running out. As we have seen, Hutton's second volume appeared in 1795. De Saussure's third and fourth volumes followed in 1796; and they reached Hutton on his death-bed in the winter of 1796–7. According to Playfair they gave Hutton particular pleasure; but they showed no change of front in regard to the potency of subterranean fire. We read instead: 'If the underground fires had been able to upraise and overturn such enormous masses, they would have left some trace of their operation; but after the most diligent search I have been unable to discover any mineral or stone which might even be suspected to have undergone the action of these fires'. In other words, he found no volcanoes in the Western Alps.

There is much in Hutton's views on these matters that no one would now defend; but there is also much that has survived.

Hutton died in 1797; de Saussure in 1799.

Chapter 9b

HUTTON'S CHAPTER II OF VOLUME II 'THE SAME SUBJECT CONTINUED WITH EXAMPLES FROM DIFFERENT COUNTRIES'

In the last chapter we have referred to extensive views in the western Alps, which led de Saussure in 1774 to recognise similar structures in the Primitives and Secondaries. From the mountain on which he stood he could see both sides of the Alps. In Italy escarpments face the central chain from the south; in France, from the north. This is a rare sight, Hutton remarks, because the central summits are mostly inaccessible. 'It is still more rare' that a person capable of making the observations has had the opportunity of observing it.

'If strata', Hutton continues in comment, 'are to be erected from the horizontal towards the vertical position, a subterraneous power must be placed under them. . . . If indeed we are to confine this subterraneous operation to a little spot, the effect may be very distinctly perceived in one view; such as those strata elevated like the roof of a house. . . . But when the operation of this cause is to be extended to a great country, as that of the Alps, it is not easy to comprehend, as it were, in one view. . . . In this case we must generalise the particular observations with regard to the inclination of the strata and their direction. . . . There is a middle line of inclination for those erected strata in this Alpine region; as if this line had been the focus or centre of action and elevation, the strata on each side being elevated towards this line, and declined from it by descending in the opposite direction'. Hutton's point may be restated by saying that de Saussure saw in the Alps a general anticlinal structure—a term that did not exist in those days.

De Saussure was further convinced that the Alpine anticline is complex. He felt certain that he could recognise several subsidiary parallel lines that have functioned in a manner similar to that of the central axis as foci of elevation, with a primitive core and a secondary envelope; and that the phenomenon is 'common to all primitive mountains, and that it is a general law that the secondaries, which border them, rise towards them from the one side and the other. It is on the Gramont (p. 99) that I first made this observation, which was new at the time. I have verified it in numerous other mountains, not only in the Alps, but also in many other chains'.

Districts with Associated Elevation and Intrusion.

Hutton now thinks it time to turn his back on the Alps. 'Having given a view of a large stretch of country where the strata are indurated or consolidated and extremely elevated, without the least appearance of subterraneous fire or volcanic productions, it will now be proper to compare with this another tract of country, where the strata, though not erected to that extreme degree, have nevertheless been evidently elevated, and, which is principally to the present purpose, are superincumbent on immense beds of basaltes or subterraneous lava'.

Hutton conducts us to the Rhine and the Meuse, and for leaders, in matters of observation rather than interpretation, relies on de Luc and Monnet. Alpine observations, Hutton recalls, have shown 'effects without the means by which those effects had been produced'. Rhineland exhibits, according to him, an association of both effects and means: uplifted sediments and subterranean basalt. One need scarcely labour the point that he was in large measure guessing.

In concluding his Chapter II Hutton explains: 'Were it necessary, much more might be given, having many examples in this country of Scotland, in Derbyshire, and in Wales, from my proper observation; but, in giving examples for the confirmation of this theory, I thought it better to seek for such as could not be suspected of partiality in the observation'. Hence, in a total of 567 pages in Volume II of his *Theory,* we find 256 devoted to quotations, mostly from de Saussure.

Chapter 9c

HUTTON'S CHAPTER III OF VOLUME II 'FACTS IN CONFIRMATION OF THE THEORY RESPECTING THOSE OPERATIONS WHICH REDISOLVE THE SURFACE OF THE EARTH'

'The next object of our research is to see those operations, belonging to the surface of the earth, by which the consolidated and erected strata have been again disolved, in order to serve the purpose of this world, and to descend again into the bottom of the sea from whence they came'.

The most interesting part of the ensuing discussion is provided by a warning from Hutton that what we see in nature may have been achieved under conditions that have locally passed away. 'It must not be imagined that, from the present state of things, we may always be able to explain every particular appearance of the kind which occurs; for example, why upon an eminence, or the summit of a ridge of land which declines on every side, an enormous mass of travelled soil appears; of why in other places, where the immediate cause is equally unseen, the solid strata should be exposed almost naked to our view. We know the agents which nature has employed for those purposes . . . and when we find the marks of those natural operations in places where, according to the present circumstances, the proper agents could not have acted or existed, we are hereby constrained to believe, that the circumstances of those places have been changed, while the operations of nature are the same'.

One feels that Hutton would have liked to invoke glaciers as he did at Mont Blanc, and, less clearly, at the Brocken (pp. 81, 107, 111), but that he had been held back because he had seen similar phenomena in Scotland, at low levels and far out of sight of any existing glacier. We must not stress this possibility unduly, for the next instance, which Hutton cites of present effects dating back to past circumstances, does not seem to have suggested to him any glacial interpretation. De Saussure had described incomprehensible moulding and striation running along the steep face of the Salève. Today we all recognise the phenomenon as a product of glaciation, but Hutton thought otherwise: 'We are now tracing a former state of things; and those furrowed rocks testify the former current of a river by their side'. De Saussure had not discussed this possibility; but had pointed out that the striation pattern could not have been engraved by rain water far above the reach of any river of today. Rain guttering would have run down the declivity, not along it.

Chapter 9d

HUTTON'S CHAPTER IV OF VOLUME II 'THE SAME SUBJECT CONTINUED IN GIVING STILL FARTHER VIEWS OF THE DISSOLUTION OF THE EARTH'

'To have an idea of this operation of running water changing the surface of the earth, one should travel in the Alps'.

Then follow 22 delightful pages lifted from the anonymous *Tableau de la Suisse.* They describe the St. Gothard Pass leading to Italy; and they certainly give an impressive picture, alike of the scenery and of the erosion which has developed it. They also remind us of the revulsion with which wild rocks and gorges were apt to be viewed as the time of writing—'There are unfortunates who can only see the dangers'.

In summary, we are told that 'examination of what passes daily before our eyes, cannot leave any doubt as to the wearing down of mountains. There is not a torrent, not any flow of water, however small, but carries away earth, with gravel, or sand to lower levels'; and (we are told on a previous page) the debris, 'as it travels farther and farther from its origin, loses its angles and salients and finishes by assuming a form, round or nearly round, according to its hardness'.

Most of what is said in these 22 pages is in keeping with Hutton's own philosophy; but is it disappointing to find him presently maintaining that thoroughly round pebbles 'could not be thus worn by travelling in the longest river'. He offers a much more complicated explanation, in which 'great roundness' must always be ascribed 'to the waves of the sea upon some former coast'. At the same time he does recognise considerable rounding during river transport.

Other quotations show that similar conditions hold elsewhere. Herodotus and Aristotle have realised this much in relation to the Nile—'that is why the Ethiopians brag that Egypt is indebted to them for its origin.' Also in front of the Pyrenees 'nature changes continually the surface of our globe; it raises plains, lowers mountains; and water is the principal agent employed to operate these great revolutions; it requires only time to realise the words of Louis XIV addressed to his son-in-law. One day posterity will be able to say; *the Pyrenees are no more.'* Gensanne has estimated a lowering of 10 inches a century; but Hutton thinks this an exaggeration: 'We have mountains in this country, and those not made of more durable materials than what are common to the earth, which are not sensibly diminished in their height with a thousand years. The proof of this are the Roman roads made over some of those hills. I have seen those roads as distinct as if only made a few years, with superficial pits beside them, from whence had been dug the gravel or materials from which they had been formed.'

Lakes are now mentioned. 'The general tendency of the operation of water upon the surface of this earth is to form plains of lakes, and not, contrarily, lakes of plains'. Lake basins may have originated during irregular upheaval of strata to form land, or through blockage by landslip or deformation by earthquake, or dissolution of saline substances.

Zig-Zag Valleys are introduced by Hutton under the title of 'correspondent angles of the valleys among mountains', or, as we should say, valleys with overlapping spurs. After illustrating by quotation the different views of Bourguet (see our p. 123) and de Luc, Hutton maintains that the operations concerned are destructive, and have acted after the formation of the mountains involved. The valleys were made by true rivers, not floods from the sea. Thus 'whether we examine the mountain or the plain; whether we consider the degradation of the rocks, or the softer strata of the earth; whether we contemplate nature, and the operations of time, upon the shores of the sea, or in the middle of the continent, in fertile countries, or in barren deserts, we shall find evidence of a general dissolution on the surface of the earth'.

Chapter 9e

HUTTON'S CHAPTER V OF VOLUME II 'FACTS IN CONFIRMATION OF THE THEORY RESPECTING THE OPERATIONS OF THE EARTH EMPLOYED IN FORMING SOIL FOR PLANTS'

'We may now', says Hutton, 'turn our view to that part of the system in which an indefinite variety of soils, for the growth of plants and life of animals, is to be provided on the face of the earth, corresponding to that diversity which, in the wisdom of nature, has been made of climates'.

He starts 'with regard to the gravel or stones worn by attrition, which may have come from a distance. In proportion as hard and insoluble stones are near to their natural beds, they will be found with the sharp angles of their fracture, unless there may have been a cause of agitation and attrition on the spot. . . . Around London, in all directions, immense quantities of gravel are found, which consist almost entirely of flint worn or rounded by attrition'. In his opinion the rounding of the pebbles is greater than would be accomplished by rivers, considering that chalk outcrops are comparatively close at hand. He therefore thinks that the pebbles were subjected to 'agitation and attrition on the spot' during marine submersion. This, however, does not affect two main points which Hutton was developing, namely: the immensity of erosion which has concentrated chalk flints into flint gravels; and the extensive transport of these gravels far beyond the limits of the chalk outcrops of England, France and Flanders.

The London gravels, we now know, constitute river terraces belonging to the Thames. Other deposits which Hutton attributed to a slight, relatively late, marine submergence are: the shelly sands of the 'Crag' of East Anglia (Early Pleistocene); the Recent raised beaches of the Firths of Forth and Cromarty; and the Glacial gravels of the English Midlands.

Transport of Erratics

We are now returned to the Alps, where a quotation informs us of unsolved difficulties which beset anyone who wishes to explain the distribution of what we now call erratics. Hutton's comment is that these wanderers, in many cases, must have travelled along routes now rendered impracticable by subsequent erosion.

An alternative explanation is quoted from de Saussure to account for boulders of Mont Blanc granite stranded in the high valleys of the Juras. De Sassure invoked a 'vast *débacle,* or general flood', capable of transporting boulders, even across the Lake of Geneva. This emphasises a very important difference separating the philosophies of de Saussure from that of Hutton: de Saussure was a

Catastrophist, Hutton a Uniformitarian. 'There is no occasion', says Hutton, 'to have recourse to any extraordinary cause for this explanation; it must appear that all the intervening hollows, plains, and valleys, had been worn away by means of the natural operations of the surface; consequently, that, in a former period of time, there had been a practicable course in a gradual declivity from the Alps to the place where those granite masses are found deposited. In that case, it will be allowed that there are natural means for the transportation of those granite masses from the top of the Alps, by means of water and ice adhering to those masses of stone, at the same time perhaps as there were certain summits of mountains, which interrupted this communication, such as the Jura, etc.'

It is obvious that when Hutton wrote this Chapter V he was only on the way to his glacial suggestion advanced in Chapter VII of his Volume II (see our Chapter 9g, p. 111).

Torr Weathering

In the cases mentioned above, the problem has been one of transport. 'In other cases, the question may be how those blocks were formed'. Hutton now quotes a long and vivid description by Hassenfratz, 1791, of torr-weathering affecting the granite of the Central Massif of France, on a vastly bigger scale than anything seen in Cornwall. Hutton, as well he might be, was delighted at such a clear story of the importance of subaerial weathering, producing a 'proper soil . . . formed from the destruction of the solid parts'.

Chapter 9f

HUTTON'S CHAPTER VI OF VOLUME II 'A VIEW OF THE OECONOMY OF NATURE, AND NECESSITY OF WASTING THE SURFACE OF THE EARTH, IN SERVING THE PURPOSES OF THIS WORLD'

'There is not perhaps one circumstance, in the constitution of this terraqueous globe, more necessary to the present theory, than to see clearly that the solid land must be destroyed, in undergoing the operations which are natural to the surface of the earth, and in serving the purposes which are necessary in the system of this living world. . . . From the bare rock exposed to the sun and wind, to the tender mud immersed in water, there is a series to be observed; and in every stage or step of this gradation, there are plants adapted to those various soils or situations. Therefore nothing short of that diversity of soils and situations, which we find upon the surface of the earth, could fulfil the purpose of nature, in producing a system of vegetables endued with such a diversity of forms and habits. The soil or surface of this earth is no more properly contrived for the life and sustenance of plants, than are those plants for that diversity of animals, which will thus appear to be the peculiar care of nature in forming a world. . . . The surface of this earth, which is so wisely adapted to the purpose of an extensive system of vegetating bodies and breathing animals, must consist of a gradation from solid rock to tender earth, from watery soil to dry situations; all this is requisite, and nothing short of this can fulfil the purpose of that world which we actually see'.

'Stripped of its dress of design, the above conveys the information that Hutton has seen many different types of deposits resulting from weathering of pre-existent rocks; and that he has realised that they serve the needs of a variety of natural associations of plants and animals. In some respects he thinks that de Luc has furnished an excellent account of the development of what the latter calls vegetable earth; and accordingly he quotes him—but, as we shall see, with an important reservation. Starting with attack and disintegration of uncovered rocks, de Luc tells us how 'rains and dew everywhere form deposits which provide the prime source of all vegetations. The deposits are always mixed with the seeds of mosses [and lichens], which the air continually carries. These are soon joined by seeds of grasses, that supply the dominant plants of our meadows'.

De Luc's agents of erosion include frost, congealing *with expansion* water that has found its way into crevices. 'V.M. feroit étonnée de la grandeur des masses que cette cause peut mouvoir: elle agit exactement la poudre à canon dans les mines.' I quote here in the original French addressed to Votre Majestée, since the letters V.M. recall the quaint fact that de Luc's correspondence was directed in the first instance to Queen Charlotte.

Similarly, de Luc points out that a tree rooted in a crack may, through growth, wedge off a mass of rock; but in the main he is impressed by the conservative function of vegetation. Plants 'tend to check the flow of water supplied by rain and dew, and thus to arrest the nutritive deposits—the vegetable earth. . . . What a richness in the resources of nature! Weight is no more ready to drag down stones that have been detached from the mountains, than is the air to furnish seeds that settle on the ground. Once rocks are covered by plants, they are certainly fixed for all time, safe at least from injury from the air. . . . Such is the simple devise employed so admirably by the Creator to preserve his handiwork'. Thus de Luc thought that erosion would cease as soon as slopes had become ameliorated to such an extent as to allow the establishment of a covering of plants.

Hutton would not admit this. He realised that vegetation often sheltered underlying material; but for him this meant more slackening, not cessation of erosion. 'According to the doctrine of this author [de Luc], our mountains of Tweed-dale and Teviotdale, being all covered with vegetation, are arrived at the period in the course of times when they should be permanent. But is it really so? Do they never waste? Look at rivers in a flood—if these run clear, this philosopher has reasoned right, and I have lost my argument. [But] our clearest streams run muddy in a flood. The great causes, therefore, for the degradation of mountains never stop as long as there is water to run; although as the heights of mountains diminish, the progress of their diminution may be more and more retarded.'

Chapter 9g

HUTTON'S CHAPTER VII OF VOLUME II 'THE SAME SUBJECT CONTINUED, IN GIVING A VIEW OF THE OPERATIONS OF AIR AND WATER, UPON THE SURFACE OF THE LAND'

Hutton's Chapter VII is a strange mixture. It mostly consists of a philosophical debate, in which readers are asked to decide between the appeal of his own and de Luc's theories of the earth—as interpretations of divine purpose. Hutton's theory holds that the earth is perfect at present, and is running in cyclic fashion to maintain its perfection through an immensity of time that shows no vestige of a beginning—no prospect of an end. De Luc's, on the other hand, envisages an earth that started only a few thousand years ago, and which will only reach perfection when vegetation has climbed eroded summits and put an end to the waste that today we see in mountainous regions. 'How', asks Hutton, 'can a philosopher, who is so much employed in contemplating the beauty of nature, the wisdom and goodness of Providence, allow himself to entertain such mean ideas of the system as to suppose, that, in the indefinite succession of time past, there has not been perfection in the works of nature?'

There are very few geological points in the long harangue which have not already been dealt with in preceding chapters; and we need not trouble with them further. Let us turn instead to what Hutton has to say of former glaciers (see pp. 81, 104, 108).

Glaciers of the Past

The good part of his Chpater VII is found at and near its beginning. It concerns the first ennunciation of the idea of a former great extension of glaciers. We quote in full.

'We have but to enlarge our thoughts with regard to things past by attending to what we see at present, and we shall understand many things which to a more contracted view appear to be in nature insulated or to be without a proper cause; such are those great blocks of granite so foreign to the place on which they stand, and so large as to seem to have been transported by some power unnatural to the place from whence they came. We have but to consider the surface of this earth, as having been upon a higher level; as having been everywhere the beds of rivers, which had moved the matter of strata and fragments of rocks, now no more existing; and as thus disposed upon different planes, which are, like the haughs of rivers, changing in a continual succession, but changing on a scale too slow to be perceived. . . .

'Let us now consider the height of the *Alps*, in general, to have been much greater than it is at present; and this is a supposition of which we have no reason to suspect the fallacy; for, the wasted summits of those mountains attest its truth. There would then have been immense valleys of ice sliding down in all directions towards the lower country, and carrying large blocks of granite to a great distance where they would be an object of admiration to after ages, conjecturing from whence, or how they came. Such are the great blocks of granite upon the hills of *Salève*. M. de Saussure, who examined them carefully, gives demonstration of the long time during which they have remained in their present place. The lime-stone bottom around being disolved by the rain, while that which serves as the basis of these masses stands high above the rest of the rock, in having been protected from the rain. But no natural operation of the globe can explain the transportation of those bodies of stone, except the changed state of things arising from the degradation of the mountains'.

This is a very fine example of interpretation from a distance. It suffers, admittedly, from its author's invocation of very great erosion of the countryside after the glaciers had made, according to his outlook, an even descent from Mont Blanc to the Salève—but we must not ask for too much at a time (see also pp. 81, 104, 108, 113).

Chapter 9h

HUTTON'S CHAPTER VIII OF VOLUME II 'THE PRESENT FORM OF THE SURFACE OF THE EARTH EXPLAINED, WITH A VIEW OF THE OPERATION OF TIME UPON OUR LAND'

'The man of scientific observation, who looks into the chain of physical events connected with the present state of things, sees great changes that have been made, and foresees a different state that must follow in time, from the continued operation of that which actually is in nature....

'The view of this interesting subject, which I had given in the first part, published in the Transactions of the Edinburgh Royal Society, has been seen by some men of science in a light which does not allow them, it would appear, to admit the general principle which I would thereby endeavour to establish. Some contend that rivers do not travel the material of the decaying land;—why?—because they have not seen all those materials moved. Others alledge that stones and rocks may be formed upon the surface of the earth, instead of being there all in a state of decay'. Hutton then reminds us that his theory 'is necessarily founded upon the decaying nature and perishing state of all that appears to us above the surface of the sea'.

Soil may be formed from the 'solid parts below', or by 'transportation of materials from a distance'. Water, or in dry regions wind, is responsible for such transport as occurs.

'From the amazing quantity of those far travelled materials, which in many places are found upon the surface of the ground, we may with certainty conclude, that there has been a great consumption of the most hard and solid parts of the land; and therefore that there must necessarily have been a still much greater destruction of the more soft and tender substances, and the more light and subtile parts which, during those operations of water, had been floated away into the sea. This appears from the enormous quantities of stones and gravel which have been transported at distances that seem incredible, and deposited at heights above the present rivers, which renders the conveyance of those bodies altogether inconceivable by any natural operation, or impossible from the present shape of the surface. This therefore leads us to conclude, that the surface of the earth must have been greatly changed since the time of those deposites of certain foreign materials of the soil. Examples of this kind have been already given'.

Hutton is referring to the Mont Blanc–Salève story as told in the previous chapter (p. 112). What follows may be regarded as a continuation of the same tale—extended beyond the Juras, from Switzerland into France, as far as Lyons and Pontarlier. Gravels rich in Alpine blocks and pebbles have passed through great cuts that traverse the Juras. De Saussure tells us that 'towards the source of the Jura valleys, surrounded by high mountains, one sees none of these pebbles foreign to the district; instead one meets with debris from the surrounding heights. In the plains, however, and at valley exits, and even for some distance up the mountain slopes, one finds pebbles and blocks which one might say had fallen from heaven, so greatly does their nature differ from anything seen round about'. De Saussure unwittingly was giving an account of outwash phenomena, peripheral to the Swiss ice-cap of Pleistocene times.

This amazing trans-Jura invasion of material from the Alps had been interpreted as propelled by a catastrophic deluge. Hutton was able to ascribe it to normal rivers of long ago, running, locally, at levels much higher than those which we see today; but not sufficiently high to lead him to replace them, in his reconstruction, by Alpine glaciers extended to the Juras. The interruption of the Alpine invasion he attributed to the development of the Swiss Plain by conjoint erosion and subsidence.

Hutton passes on to other easily recognised examples of transportation of eroded products: of kaolin strata derived from the decomposition of granite; of tin-stone and gold, regularly followed upstream to their sources by prospectors.

Sea Erosion

'We have now to examine what is left of that solid part which had furnished the materials of our soil. . . . It is only from the examination of the present state of things that judgments may be formed, in just reasoning, concerning what has been transacted in a former period of time'—this, of course, is a reiteration of the author's doctrine of uniformity.

Hutton passes from interior land to marginal land, where land and sea make contact. He notes that high cliffs are faced by deposit-free sea, because if the sea can erode a cliff, it must also be able to clear away the resultant debris. On the other hand, where rivers discharge more material into the sea than the latter can concurrently cope with, a shelving shore results, with temporary advance of land into sea.

In north-west Europe 'the sea has made ravages upon those coasts in proportion to its power, and has left them in a shape corresponding to the composition of the land, in destroying the soft and leaving the harder parts'. Hutton sees in his mind's eye that 'peninsulas are gradually detached from the main land, in thus forming islands, which are but little removed from the land. . . . These islands again, in being subdivided, are converted into barren rocks, which point out to us the course in which the lost or wasted land upon the coast had formerly existed'. Hutton gives several examples at home and abroad to illustrate his remarks, including an account of a violent storm on the Italian coast, and a quaint, previously unpublished letter from the Rev. William Hamilton regarding the shores of Antrim.

Chapter 9i

HUTTON'S CHAPTER IX OF VOLUME II 'THE THEORY ILLUSTRATED, WITH A VIEW OF THE SUMMITS OF THE ALPS'

'We have been considering the incroachment of the sea upon the continent; let us now examine how far there may also appear sufficient documents, by which we may be led to conclude a long progress in time past, for the destruction of the solid mass of earth above the sea, without diminishing its basis'.

Mining has often supplied a 'measured minimum of the quantity which had been removed. . . . The coal strata, about Newcastle on Tyne, dip to the south-east at the rate of one in twelve, or thereabouts. This is but little removed from the horizontal position; at the same time, the strata came all up to the soil or surface in a country which is level, or with little risings. But in those strata there is a slip or hitch, which runs from north-east to south-west, for 17 or 18 miles in a straight line; the surface on each side of this line is perfectly equal, and nothing distinguishable in the soil above; but in sinking mines the same strata are found at the distance of 70 fathoms form each other. Here therefore is a demonstration, that there had been worn away, and removed into the sea, 70 fathoms more from the country on the one side of this line, than from that on the other. It is far from giving us all the height of country which has been washed away, but it gives us a minimum of that quantity'.

In Alpine country 'the ravages of weather in destroying the solid parts of the globe in order to make soil' are more marked than in the lower districts. 'On whatever side we approach the Alps, we find some great river discharging the waters which had been gathered above, and with that water all the waste of earth and stone which had been made among those normal lofty masses of decaying rock'. This leads Hutton on to trace a normal pattern for a big drainage basin. In the first place, the trunk river is generally 'proportioned' to its containing valley. 'The question occurs; Has this valley been made by the operation of the river itself, or has it been the effect of other causes?'

River Systems

As we ascend 'we find other valleys branching from this main valley; and, in all those subordinate valleys, we find rivers corresponding in like manner with the magnitude of the valley [see p. 127]. Here, therefore, is infinitely more than a single river, and a valley corresponding to the river; here is a *system* of rivers and of valleys, things calculated in perfect wisdom, or properly adapted to each other'. It is only on an erosion theory 'that such a complicated operation, of a series in rivers and their valleys, is to be explained' —furnishing 'a system in which is manifested wisdom, so far as all the parts are properly adapted to each other'.

'In thus tracing rivers and their branchings, we come at last to rivulets that only run in times of rain, and at other times are dry. It is here that I would wish to carry my reader, in order to be convinced, with his proper observation, of this great fact—that the rivers, in general, have hollowed out their valleys. . . .

'The changes of the valley of the main river are but slow, the plain indeed is wasted in one place, but it is repaired in another, and we do not perceive the place from whence that repairing matter had proceeded. . . . But it is otherwise in the valley of the rivulet; no person can examine this subject without seeing that the rivulet carries away matter which cannot be repaired except by wearing away some part of the mountain, or the surface of that place upon which the rain, which forms the stream, is gathered'.

That valleys are in general proportioned to their rivers or streams, trunk or tributary, is indeed a most significant fact pointing indubitably to erosion. In latter days, the great geographer W. M. Davis has bestowed upon it the title *Playfair's Law*. Playfair had given an excellent account of it in his *Illustrations of the Huttonian Theory;* but his presentation was essentially a reproduction.

Glacier Systems

It is interesting to find Hutton, climbing higher, metaphorically, in the Alps, where 'there is another system of valleys, above that of the rivers, and connected with it. These are valleys of moving ice, instead of water. This icy valley is also found branching from a greater to a lesser, until at last it ends upon the summit of a mountain covered continually with snow. The motion of things in those valleys is commonly exceeding slow, the operation however ... of fracture and attrition, is extremely powerful'.

Aiguilles

Hutton now takes his reader to the neighbourhood of Mont Blanc, using as so often, de Saussure's descriptions as a magic carpet, in this case supplemented by two drawings reproduced in the original as plates. De Saussure is particularly impressed by the marvellous aiguilles, or needles, of the district. He thinks they may be fashioned out of hard kernels which have preferentially resisted the ravages of weather; but he is ready to discuss, presently, how far 'crystallisation may have contributed to determine these pyramidal forms? Should one consider Mont Blanc, or some other *aiguille,* as an enormous crystal?'

Hutton has no doubts: vertical joints have localised relatively rapid vertical erosion resulting in chasms which, connectedly, drain downhill. The chasms slowly open up, largely by frost action, so that the stronger material between the master joints assumes pyramidal form. Hutton's answer is in a sense a variant of de Saussure's first alternative; 'but', he cries out, 'what a waste of rock to have formed all those needles which we find rising from the icy valleys round Mont Blanc. . . .'

'From the top of those decaying pyramids to the sea, we have a chain of facts which clearly demonstrate this proposition, that the materials of the wasted mountains have travelled through the rivers; for, in every step of this progress, we may see the effect, and thus acknowledge the proper cause. We may often be witness to the action; but it is only a small part of the whole progress that we may thus perceive, nevertheless it is equally satisfactory as if we saw the whole, for, throughout the whole of this long course, we may see some part of the mountain moving some part of the way. What more can we require? Nothing but time'.

Chapter 9j

HUTTON'S CHAPTER X OF VOLUME II 'THE THEORY ILLUSTRATED WITH A VIEW OF THE VALLEYS OF THE ALPS'

Hutton with copious quotations, mostly referring to the Alps, supplies additional illustrations of the universality of erosion upon the surface of the land. 'But with what wisdom is that destroying power disposed! The summit of the mountain is degraded, and the materials of this part, which in a manner has become useless from its excessive height, are employed in order to extend the limits of the shore, and thus increase the useful basis of our dwellings'.

A quotation from de Saussure conveys the special pleasure which its author found in exploring Monte Rosa; for here erosion has shaped an immense mass of gneiss and other foliated rocks, lying almost horizontal and unaccompanied by granite. It was indeed stimulating to find such a contrast with Mont Blanc, where vertical beds and abundant granite are so highly characteristic.

American Support.—A most unusual feature, and one not suggested by the title of Hutton's Chapter X, is the introduction of a supporting quotation from across the Atlantic. It was taken from Thomas Jefferson's *Notes on Virginia,* 1781, an essentially political publication. The part quoted is concerned, in the first place, with a gorge cut across the Blue Ridge downstream from Harper's Ferry, where the Potomac is joined by the Shenandoah—55 miles N.W. of Washington. The author of the *Notes* was a versatile statesman (1743-1826) who, some years previously, had drafted the *Declaration of Independence,* 1776, and who, in years to come, was destined to be elected third President of the U.S.A., 1801–1809. Outside his political interests, Jefferson was a keen student of natural history.

'The passage of the Potomac, through the Blue Ridge', he says, 'is perhaps one of the most stupendous scenes in nature. . . . The first glance of this scene hurries our senses into the opinion, that this earth had been erected in time; that the mountains were formed first; that the rivers began to flow afterwards; that in this place particularly they have been dammed up by the Blue Ridge of mountains, and have formed an ocean which filled the whole valley; that, continuing to rise, they have at length broken over this spot, and have torn the mountain down from its summit to its base. The piles of rock on each hand, but particularly on the Shenandoah, the evident marks of this disrupture and avulsion from their beds, by the most powerful agents of nature, corroborate the impression. . . . This scene is worth a voyage across the Atlantic. . . . It is a war between the rivers and mountains, which must have shaken the earth itself to its center'.

Hutton's comment on Jefferson's assumption that the mountains were formed first, the rivers after, is faultless: 'So far as rivers, in their course from the higher to the lower country, move bodies with the force of their rolling waters, and clear away the solid strata of the earth, we must consider rivers as also forming mountains, at least as forming the valleys which are co-relative in what is termed *mountain*.'

He comes near to agreeing that the scene is worth a transatlantic voyage, when he says: 'I have often admired, in the map, that wonderful regularity with which those mountains are laid down, and I have much wished for a sight of that gap, through which the rivers, gathered in the long valleys of those mountains, break through the ridge and find a passage to the sea.'

As regards Jefferson's suggestion of a catastrophe shaking 'the earth itself to its centre', Hutton remarks: 'How little reason there is to ascribe to extraordinary convulsions the excavations which are made by water upon the surface of the earth, will appear most evidently from examination of that natural bridge', which near Bridgeton, spans the Cedar Creek, one of the head-waters of the James River. Long worshipped by Indians, it was surveyed by George Washington about 1750, and it still carries his initials. In 1774, along with 157 adjacent acres, it was bought by Jefferson from George III for 'twenty shillings of good and lawful money.' During the revolutionary war, for lack of a shot-tower, molten lead was dropped from the bridge to make bullets for the Colonists. Since then, Henry Clay (1777–1852), great statesman and compromise emancipator, has described it as follows: 'The Bridge not made by hands, God's great stone masterpiece, spans a creek, carries a national highway and makes two mountains one. It is 90 feet long, 60 feet broad and 215 feet above the river which flows under it'.

'Though the sides of the bridge', to return to Jefferson, 'are provided in some parts with a parapet of fixed rock, yet few men have the resolution to walk to them, and look over into the abyss. You involuntarily, fall on your hands and feet, and creep to the parapet, and look over it. Looking down from this height about a minute gave me a violent headache. If the view from the top be painful and intolerable, that from below is delightful in the extreme'.

It is difficult from the above account to understand how the bridge originated—it is probably a solution-phenomenon, short-circuiting a waterfall, for Jefferson says that the country-rock here is limestone. At any rate, Hutton is almost certainly right in not accepting Jefferson's view, that is resulted from 'some great convulsion'.

Jefferson includes in an appendix to his *Notes on Virginia* an account of the Harper's Ferry gorge by Thomson, Secretary to Congress. It follows the same lines as his own; but as an additional feature surmises that the Delaware, 80 miles to the north, once 'passed through what is now called the Wind-gap', towards the Susquehana. Wind-gap has since established itself firmly in the vocabulary of geologists and geographers; while Harper's Ferry has achieved an important place in national history. Its geographical position led to the establishment of an arsenal in its precincts; and this, in 1859, attracted the world-famous raid by John Brown, whose soul goes marching on. The Civil War followed in 1861; and a year later Stonewall Jackson secured at Harper's Ferry a crippling surrender of 12,520 Federal troops—which, of course, did not bring victory to the Confederates in the end.

Chapter 9k

HUTTON'S CHAPTER XI OF VOLUME II 'FACTS AND OPINIONS CONCERNING THE NATURAL CONSTRUCTION OF MOUNTAINS AND VALLEYS'

The question arises: have the features of the Rhone country above Lake Geneva been determined by the movement that upheaved the mountain-land; or have 'the destructive causes, which operate at degrading mountains, ... immediately contributed to produce their present forms?' De Saussure is called as a witness that the valleys of the Alps have, for the most part, been eroded; and that the agents employed have often been, not currents of the sea, but ordinary rivers of the land. On the other hand, de Saussure thinks that some valleys have been directly located by earth-movement, where partial subsidence has modified upheaval. For instance, he thinks the Val d'Aosta has been determined by earth-movement, because the disposition of bedding on its two sides conforms with the flow both of the river and of its tributaries. Here Hutton disagrees a little with de Saussure's opinion, or at least, from the manner in which it is expressed: 'We cannot', he says, 'suppose any river formed by another agent than the running water upon the surface, although the parts which are first to be washed away, and those which are to remain longest, must be determined by a concurrence of various circumstances, among which this converging declivity of the strata in the bordering mountains, doubtless, must be enumerated. . . .

'The particular forms of mountains depend upon the compound operation of two very different causes. One of these consists in those mineral operations by which the strata of the earth are consolidated and displaced, or disordered in the production of land above the sea; the other again consists in those meteorological operations by which the earth is rendered a habitable world. . . .

'In explaining those appearances of degraded mountains variously shaped, the fact that we are now to reason upon is this; first, that in the consolidated earth we find great inequality in the resisting powers of the various consolidated bodies, both from the different degrees of consolidation which had taken place among them, and the different degrees of solubility in the consolidated substances; and, secondly, that we find great diversity in the size, form, and position of those most durable bodies which, by resisting longer the effects of the wearing operations of the surface, must determine the shape of the remaining mass. . . .

'We are to distinguish mountains as being on the one hand soft and smooth, or on the other hand as hard and rocky. . . . The soft and smooth mountains are generally formed of the schisti. . . . Of this kind are the schisti of Wales, of Cumberland, of the Isle of Man, and of the south of Scotland. . . . It may be also formed of any other substance which has solidity enough to remain in the form of mountains, and at the same time not enough to form salient rocks. Such, for example, is the chalk hills of the Isle of Wight and south of England. . . . Such mountains are necessarily composed of rounded masses, and not formed of angular shapes. . . .

'With regard to the other species of mountain, which we have termed rocky, we must make a subdistinction of those which are regular, and those in which there is no regularity to be perceived.' It is only the regular types that are considered below. If the material of a regular mountain is uniform, there is a tendency for weathering to give 'a conical or pyramidical form'; if the material is stratified with beds of different degrees of durability, the 'destructive forces of the surface' are guided by dip: horizontal stratification leads to the formation of tablelands (as Bouguer—see p. 123—has shown); inclined stratification to scarp on one side, gentle slope on the other (de Saussure); and vertical stratification, to rocky ridges bounded on both sides by steep slopes.

Hutton also distinguishes between 'associated' and 'insulated' mountains: the associated owe their form, though not their height above sea level, to erosion; the insulated, so far as they are modern volcanoes, owe most of both form and height to accretion. In addition there are insulated mountains, well displayed in the Midland Valley of Scotland (Hutton quotes North Berwick Law and Salisbury Crags as examples). Many of them—he thinks all—are subterranean lavas, laid bare from top to bottom by erosion.

Rhone Erosion.—Perhaps the most important feature of the quotations from de Saussure, which Hutton includes in his unusually interesting Chapter XI, concerns the vast erosion attributable to the Rhone downstream from Martigny. De Saussure points out that the elements combined in the Dents du Midi, west of the river, correspond so closely with those in the Dent de Morcles, east of the same, that they must once have been continuous, though now severed by the great Rhone Valley.

Roches Moutonnées.—Another quotation from de Saussure (§ .1061 in his *Voyages*) describes the mountains through which the Rhone has made its way out of the Alps at the end of the *Vallée*. 'Farther from the village of *Juviana* or Envionne one sees rocks which have a form I call *moutonné*. . . . They are composed of an assemblage of rounded heads. . . . These are hillocks, contiguous and repeated, that give the impression, on a large scale, of a thick fleece or of those wigs which one also calls moutonné'. Subsequent usage has shifted this term, in geology, from an assemblage of humps to each individual hump in such an assemblage; and has changed its meaning from *frizzy* to *sheeplike* (E. J. Garwood, 1932, *Pres. Address*).

There is, of course, no need, nor possibility, to go back in this matter to the original. Modern usage has also decided that a *roche moutonnée* is shaped by glacial erosion—a fact that was completely hidden from de Saussure.

Chapter 9l

HUTTON'S CHAPTER XII OF VOLUME II 'THE THEORY ILLUSTRATED, BY ADDUCING EXAMPLES FROM THE DIFFERENT QUARTERS OF THE GLOBE'

'The system which we investigate', says Hutton, 'is universal; . . . but this the reader is not to take upon my bare assertion; and I would wish to carry him, by the observations of other men, to all the quarters of the globe'.

The first guide, whom Hutton selects is for this purpose Marsden, writing of the coastal plain of Sumatra; but his testimony does not seem very impressive. The second is the famous mathematician and geodesist Pierre Bouguer (1698–1758), whom we have already met in the course of these pages (106, 122). In 1735 Bouguer was sent by the Paris Academy of Sciences to measure a degree of meridian near the Equator. The result was to be compared with a similar measurement in Lapland to settle a controversy as to whether the earth were oblate or prolate. The oblate partisans won the day; and gravity observations made during the research marked the first step taken towards the conception of isostasy.

Hutton's interest in Bouguer's findings concerned neither the form of the earth as a whole, nor variations of its gravity, but rather the degradations brought about by erosion. Bouguer had been surprised to find, a little east of the cordillera, some fifteen hundred feet of horizontal sediments 'continually assuming the appearance of keeps and sumptuous edifices, of chapels, domes and chateaus. . . . It is difficult when one observes all these objects, and the manner in which their beds correspond, to doubt that the surface has sunk all around. It appears that those mountains with foundations more solidly placed have been left as a kind of witness or monument to the height of the soil'. Hutton, quite properly, could not accept this hypothesis. His own interpretation 'belongs to the present Theory, which represents the action of running water upon the surface of the earth as instrumental in producing its particular forms'.

Hutton continues: 'Naturalists, who have examined the various parts of the earth, almost all agree in this, that great effects have been produced by water upon the surface of the earth. . . . Some suppose great catastrophes to have occasioned sudden changes upon the surface, in having removed immense quantities of the solid body, and in having deposited parts of the removed mass at great distances from their original beds, . . . The theory of the earth which I would here illustrate is founded upon the greatest catastrophes which can happen to the earth, that is, in being raised from the bottom of the sea, . . . and in being sunk again from its elevated station under that mass of water from which it had originally come. But the changes which we are now investigating have no further relation to those great catastrophes, except in so far as these great operations of the globe have put the solid land in such a situation as to be affected by the atmospheric influences and operations of the surface'. (Although Hutton in this passage speaks of catastrophies, I think that he imagined these catastrophes as having been conducted in stages such as are characteristic of modern earthquake activity.)

Hutton then introduces a 17-page account, which Reboul read to the Academy of Sciences in Paris, 1788. It describes the wild valley leading up from the French plain at the foot of the Pyrenees to the magnificent cirque or corrie of Gavarnie, close to the Spanish frontier. Reboul's description is delightful, and full of river erosion, thus illustrating what Hutton has said in the previous paragraph, about its recognition in many parts of the world. One feels, however, in reading it, and others of its kind, that the work of glaciers and glacial outwash is frequently described without separation from that of rivers such as we see today. The Glacial Period was an unsuspected catastrophe of the past. Hutton, as we have seen, touched upon the fringe of this subject—but no more. In commenting on Reboul he complains that the latter has introduced an unnecessarily big landslip into his restoration of the story of the Gavarnie valley; but on the whole he is well pleased with it.

Le Blond, 1786, takes us back to South America, this time well up in the Andes, a little south of the Equator. Here 11 pages of quotation clearly show recognition of river erosion; though more thought seems to have been given to absence of fish at high levels.

Waterfalls and cold are given as partial causes; to which we may presumably add scarcity of oxygen.

D. Ullua continues with the high Andes north of the Equator. We read, for instance, of 'what will necessarily happen at the gorge of the Canaica, when, with the lapse of time, the effects of rain, frost and sunshine will have made its vertical walls tumble in ruin.' We are also told that a great deal has happened 'since the deluge', which for him probably meant 'since Noah's flood', but for us 'since the Ice Age'.

Monnet has already been introduced (p. 89). Here a quotation is taken from the *Journal de Physique,* 1781, dealing with the province of Hainault in Belgium. Monnet gives excellent accounts of river wastage of a plateau, including the wonderful gorge-cutting of the Meuse. An interesting feature is that erosional phenomena, both here and in France, sometimes seem to him too big to be referred to the streams and rivers of today with their present volumes, even though he is prepared to reckon time in 'thousands of centuries'. He therefore suggests that river volumes have been reduced in correlation with the shrinkage of oceans—which last we have already noted as a fundamental conception of the Neptunists.

Hutton's reply was: 'This opinion of M. Monnet, concerning the diminution of water upon the earth, does not follow necessarily from the appearances which he has mentioned. The surface of the earth is certainly changed by the gradual operations of the running water, and it may not be unfrequent to find a small stream of water in places where a greater stream had formerly run'.

Chapter 9m

HUTTON'S CHAPTER XIII OF VOLUME II 'THE SAME SUBJECT CONTINUED'

Submarine Lavas of Subterraneous Intrusions

Hutton starts his Chapter XIII with an 8-page quotation from de Dolomieu, 1784, in which 'the operation of water wasting the land

and forming valleys' is subordinated to igneous interests. Dolomieu has found in the Val de Nota, south of Syracuse in Sicily, what he takes to be a succession of submarine lavas, separated by limestone full of shells and corals. The resultant complex, he thinks, was raised and extensively eroded 'during the great debacle or catastrophe which altered the emplacement of the sea'. Hutton, in accordance with his often-mistaken views in such matters, reinterprets the igneous rocks as intrusions; he also regards the erosion of the complex as quietly subaerial, following, rather than accompanying, upheaval from the sea.

Further quotations, however, are mostly limited to erosional matters, based upon: Sir William Hamilton, 1786, Apennines; Pallas, Russia; DeGy, 1787, Juras; De la Metherie, 1787, France (illustrated by a 'mineral map', utilised but not reproduced by Hutton). The latter's reactions may be grouped together under three headings as follows.

(1) *Lake Problem:* 'If there is so much of the solid parts worn and washed away upon the surface of this earth, as represented in our Theory; and if the rivers have run for so long in their proper courses, it may perhaps be demanded, why are not all the lakes filled up with soil? . . .

'It must be evident, that the objection to the Theory, here supposed to be made, is founded necessarily upon this, that the solid basis of our continent, on whose surface are found the lakes in question, is preserved without change'. In other words, Hutton points out that lake formation may temporarily interrupt river erosion. Such lake formation he has already ascribed to a variety of causes: to subsidence of the lake site due to earth movement or to solution; and to the building of a dam by earth movement or by landslip; and, if he had been able to foresee Andrew Ramsay's great paper of 1862, he might have added, as frequent causes, glacial erosion and morainic blocking.

Hutton notices that, where his critics claim to have recognised the draining of a hypothetical great lake of the past, they 'seem to be disposed to attribute to some great convulsion, rather than to the slow operation of a rivulet, those changes which may be observed upon the surface of the earth'. Needless to say, he himself prefers the rivulet.

Hutton warns us against accepting at face value all the basins which look as though they had formerly been occupied by lakes. They may be broad and open with alluvial bottoms, and they may drain through a transversal ridge of hard rock by way of a relatively narrow gap. It is often assumed that a gorge of this kind has been eroded through the transverse ridge *as we see it today;* 'but', says Hutton, 'it is more natural to assume that the great gap of the Loire or the Rhone was formed gradually in proportion as the included [upstream] country had been worn down and transported to the sea'. This is a splendid idea already communicated to us at Harper's Ferry (p. 118). We find it repeated a couple of pages further on in regard to another locality. 'There is no difficulty in conceiving that the river, which must wear away a passage through those mountains, should also hollow out the [upstream] softer materials within, and thus form the plain, or rather a succession of plains, in proportion as the level of the water had been lowered with the wearing mountains'.

(2) *Tributaries:* Hutton reinforces his conception of a river system with an adjusted scheme of tributaries (p. 116). Below we reproduce some characteristic passages.

De la Metherie's mineral map is valuable as 'a plan of the valleys of the great rivers and their various branches, which, however, infinitely ramified, may be considered as forming each one great valley watered, or rather drained, by its proper river'.

'Thus there is a system of mountains and valleys, of hills and plains, of rivulets and rivers, all of which are so perfectly connected, and so admirably proportioned, in their forms and quantities, like the arteries and veins of the animal body, that it would be absurd to suppose that anything but wisdom could have designed this system of the earth, in delivering water to run from the higher ground.

'No man can say, by looking into the most perfect map, what is primary or what secondary, in the constitution of the globe. It is the same system of larger rivers branching into lesser and lesser in a continued series, of smaller rivers in like manner branching into rivulets, and of rivulets terminating at last into springs or temporary streams. The principle is universal'.

'If we consider our continent as composed of such materials as may decay by the influence of the atmosphere, and be moved by water descending from the higher to the lower ground, as is actually the case with the land of our globe, then the water would gradually form channels, in which it would run from place to place, and those channels continually uniting as they proceed to the sea or shore, would form a system of rivers and their branchings. But this system of moving water must gradually produce valleys, by carrying away stones and earthy matter in their floods; and those valleys would be changing according to the softness and hardness, destructability or indestructability of the solid parts below. Still however the system of valley and river would be preserved; and to this would be added the system of mountains and valleys, of hills and plains, to the formation of which the unequal wearing down of the solids must in a great measure contribute'.

(3) *Not oceanic:* 'To suppose the currents of the ocean to have formed that system of hill and dale, of branching rivers and rivulets, divided almost *ad infinitum,* which assemble together the water poured at large upon the surface of the earth, in order to nourish a great diversity of animals calculated for that moving element, and which carry back to the sea the superfluity of water, would be to suppose a systematic order in the currents of the ocean, an order which, with as much reason, we might look for in the wind.'

Chapter 9n

HUTTON'S CHAPTER XIV OF VOLUME II 'SUMMARY OF THE DOCTRINE WHICH HAS BEEN NOW ILLUSTRATED'

Hutton devotes his Chapter XIV of Volume II to a summary of the two volumes which we have skimmed up to this point in our Subchapters 8a–h and 9a–m. His first paragraph seems unexceptional, since it states: 'The system of this earth appears to comprehend many different operations; and it exhibits various powers cooperating for the production of those effects which we perceive. Of this we are informed by studying natural appearances; and in this manner we are led to understand the nature of things in knowing causes'. We are, however, told, almost at once, of the 'general system of nature, which has for object a world sustaining plants and animals'.

Hutton's 'causes' are of two kinds, both deduced, rightly or wrongly, from observation: the one group is more objective; the other, more subjective. The first is represented by the proposition that rivers cut out valleys; the second by the proposition that rivers cut out valleys to provide dry land to be occupied by plants and animals. Hutton in his summary asks us to accept both these propositions (and many others of like kind) as definitely proved. (He also gives us the impression that, if we do not accept his hypothesis that consolidation depends on partial melting under deep sea pressures, we are rejecting the most important part of his *Theory*—but that is a different story).

Admittedly Hutton muddled his presentation in Volumes I and II by mixing what he sometimes called 'moral' with 'physical' argument; but in the last three paragraphs of his Chapter XIV, Volume II, he tells us:

'In the system of the globe everything must be consistent. . . .

'A system is thus formed in generalising all those different effects, or in ascribing all those particular operations to a general end. This end, the subject of our understanding, is then to be considered as an object of design; and, in this design, we may perceive, either wisdom, so far as the ends and means are properly adapted, or benevolence, so far as the system is contrived for the benefit of beings who are capable of suffering pain and pleasure, and of judging good and evil.

'But, in this physical dissertation, we are limited to consider the manner in which things present have been made to come to pass, and not to inquire concerning the moral end for which those things may have been calculated'. With all of which most modern readers can agree.

The idea that a succession of happenings should be disentangled before it 'be considered as object of design' came late to Hutton, probably as a result of conversations with Playfair. The three paragraphs, just considered, were presumably intended to inform readers of what they must expect in Volumes III and IV.

'END OF VOLUME SECOND'

Chapter 10

1899
HUTTON'S THEORY OF THE EARTH IN BOOK FORM 'WITH PROOFS AND ILLUSTRATIONS' VOLUME III

THE STRANGE career of what, after a century of delay, has been published as Volume III of Hutton's *Theory of the Earth* has been capitally told by V. A. Eyles in the Hutton volume, 1950, of the *Proceedings of the Royal Society, Edinburgh.*

'The circumstances that led, ultimately, to the issue of Vol. III of *The Theory* in 1899 have been related by Sir Archibald Geikie in the editorial preface that he contributed to this volume; and have been amplified by the late Professor F. D. Adams of Montreal, in an address delivered to the Edinburgh Geological Society during its Centenary Celebrations in 1934. The story, though familiar to many Scottish geologists, is of general interest, and is worth recapitulating in brief, more particularly since it is possible to add a postscript.

'Playfair, in his Biographical Account of James Hutton, stated that a third volume of *The Theory* remained behind in manuscript, and at about the time of Hutton's death this M.S. seems to have passed into Playfair's keeping. Playfair showed it to Lord Webb Seymour, a keen amateur geologist, who was also a friend of Hutton, and the latter [Lord Seymour] actually quotes it in a paper that he read before the Royal Society of Edinburgh in 1814, stating that it was nearly ready for the press. Later, Playfair gave the M.S. to Lord Webb Seymour. Still later, on the death of the latter, the M.S. was handed over to Leonard Horner, a prominent geologist of the period, with Edinburgh connections, and at one time Secretary of the Geological Society of London. Horner, in 1856, presented the M.S. to this Society [London G.S.], attaching to it the following memorandum:

' "This M.S. volume (part of a series) of Hutton's with some additions in his own hand, containing six chapters of illustrations of the *Theory of the Earth,* was given to Lord Webb Seymour by Mr. Playfair (as Playfair himself told me), and after his lordship's death I received it from the Duke of Somerset when he came to Edinburgh on the occasion of his brother's decease. I gave it to the Geological Society, to be preserved in the library, as an interesting document in the history of science.—L.H. 30th Nov., 1856."

'There the M.S. lay for many years, unnoticed and forgotten. Years later Geikie became aware of its existence, possibly through the references to it made by Playfair or Webb Seymour, but for some unexplained reason he failed to locate it in the library of the Geological Society. According to Adams, he stated that for years he had searched for it in every library in which it might have found a resting place, but without success. This statement was made in the course of a dinner party in Baltimore, in 1896, at which Adams was present, and the latter thereupon informed Geikie that the missing M.S. was, in fact, safe in the keeping of the Geological Society of London, where it stood on the shelf beside the two printed volumes of *The Theory*. Adams himself had only discovered it by accident, through the fact that, during a visit to the Society's rooms, on asking for the two published volumes of *The Theory,* the attendant also handed him the supposedly lost M.S., remarking at the same time, as Adams relates, that he had found "this old thing" on the shelf beside the others and thought that possibly I might find "something of interest" in it. Professor Adams had in fact sent a letter to *Nature* announcing the discovery, but this also escaped Geikie's notice.

'Neither of these distinguished geologists can have examined the printed Catalogue of the library of the Geological Society, published some years previously in 1881, which contains the following entries: (1) At the beginning of the Catalogue, among a list of "Books not allowed to Circulate", "Hutton. Geological M.S.S.", and (2) in the Catalogue proper, opposite the name of James Hutton, "*Illustrations of the Theory of the Earth.* Chapters IV to IX inclusive. 4to. M.S.".

'Having at last, by a fortunate chance located the lost M.S., Geikie, on his return to London, lost no time in approaching the Council of the Geological Society with the suggestion that they should undertake to publish it. This they agreed to do, and it was issued as Vol. III of *The Theory of the Earth* 1899, Geikie acting as editor'.

Volume III as published, with helpful editorial preface, illustrations and footnotes, consists only of Chapters IV–IX. What has happened to Chapters I–III, amounting to 138 pages of M.S., we do not know. One common feature runs through those that have survived: they only contain a couple of inconspicuous references to design. It would appear from this, and from what has been said at the end of our Chapter 9n, that 'moral' considerations were intended to be reserved for a Volume IV, which was promised (as a Part) on the title pages of Volumes I and II.

We are told that Chapters IV, V and IX of Volume III were written in 1785, 1786 and 1787, respectively; but there are obvious additions, for a footnote to Chapter V is dated 1788, and the reading of a paper mentioned in Chapter IX, 1790.

The question naturally arises: Why had Volume III to wait so long for publication? Geikie suggests as a possible cause the loss for some reason of the sketches which the Clerks had prepared for its embellishment—to which we may reasonably add the loss also of Chapters I–III. More important still, I think, was the disappointment which Hutton's Volumes I and II brought to Playfair and other friends, when they appeared in 1795, only two years before their author's death. It was in this mood that Playfair undertook the writing of his *Illustrations of the Huttonian Theory,* 1806. In the preparation of this work Playfair does not seem to have consulted Hutton's manuscript of Volume III. Indeed it is doubtful if he ever read it all—though admittedly his friend Webb Seymour quoted from Chapter V. It is a great pity that Chapters IV, V and IX, dealing with Glen Tilt, Galloway and Arran, were not published in Hutton's lifetime, or as soon as possible after his death. They show Hutton at his best, and could scarcely have failed to accelerate the advance of geology. Chapters VI, VII and VIII, on the other hand, dealing with the Alps, Pyrennees and Calabria, would probably have done more harm than good.

We may conclude by recalling that it is on p. XV of his Preface to Volume III that Geikie speaks of Hutton as the Father of Modern Geology.

Chapter 10*a*

HUTTON'S CHAPTER IV OF HIS VOLUME III 'OBSERVATIONS MADE IN A JOURNEY TO THE NORTH ALPINE PART OF SCOTLAND IN THE YEAR 1785'

Hutton's Chapter IV of his Volume III provides an account of his 1785 investigation of Glen Tilt made in company with Clerk of Eldin. The subject has already been dealt with to some extent in our Chapter 5; and we shall avoid repetition as far as possible.

Scotland is broadly divisible into what we now call Highlands, Midland Valley and Southern Uplands. The rocks of the first and last were grouped by Hutton as Alpine schistus and granite; while those of the Midland Valley were described as later sandstones, coals, limestones, etc., accompanied by hills of whinstone exposed by erosion. The 'stretch' or 'direction', which we now call 'strike', of the Highland schistus was already known to Hutton as generally N.E.—S.W., with dips sometimes N.W., sometimes S.E.

As regards 'primary and posterior, naturalists have thought to distinguish granite as primary in relation to the schistus mountains which they thus suppose as having been formed posterior to it; but as I have just now found evidence of the contrary in a journey which I have made to the Highlands, it will not be unacceptable to the public to know the state in which those things are found.' This sentence assures us of the motive that led Hutton with Clerk of Eldin to investigate the contact relationship of granite and schistus. It also assures us (in combination with the context of 'this harvest', used two pages further on in his text as printed) that Hutton wrote much of Chapter IV before the end of 1785.

In choosing a locality for examination, Hutton had the following guides. He knew 'that in the sources of the River Dee there were great granite countries, and that in most of the sources of the Tay, nothing is to be found but the Alpine schistus; the Tay sources mentioned chiefly lie to the south-west, whereas in the bed of the Tay itself there is 'abundance of gravel formed of granite and porphyry'. All this pointed to granite and schistus meeting one another 'in the north-eastern branches of that river'.

The Duke of Atholl, who, it will be remembered, acted as host on this occasion, 'nobly supported by the most kind and hospitable assistance', made 'an agreeable party of a thing which otherwise would have been uncommodious and painful.

'It is particularly in Glen Tilt that this most interesting part of a natural history is to be seen. . . .

'On the south side of the glen, the strata are composed of alpine schistus, particularly of granulated quartz and micaceous limestone; and these strata dip into the hill in descending to the south. On the other side of the glen, the steep face of the hill is all covered with lumps of beautiful red granite, not a particle of which is to be seen on the south side. Here therefore we were upon the very spot which we desired, and fortunately for our researches, the river lays bare enough of the solid parts to give the most satisfactory view of what had been transacted in a former period. . . .

'It must be recollected that the present question regards the granite, how far it is to be considered as a primary mass in relation to the alpine schistus; in that case, fragments of the granite might be found included in the schistus, but none of the schistus in the granite. But besides this point to be ascertained, I had in a preceding part of this work drawn a very probable conclusion concerning the natural history of granite, so far as those masses might be considered as analogous to basaltes, or subterraneous lava, in having been made to flow. We have both those points now perfectly decided; the granite is now found breaking and displacing the strata in every conceivable manner, including the fragments of the broken strata, and interjected in every possible direction among the strata which appear. This is to be seen, not in one place only of the valley, but in many places, where the rocks appear, or where the river has laid bare the strata.

'Having thus ascertained this cardinal point it was necessary to explore the solid mass of granite. . . . Having, therefore, with some difficulty, mounted the precipitous bed of a rivulet that comes from this long ridge of mountain, and which is fit for no other than the footsteps of a goat, we were rewarded with a view of the strata of the hill, being a perpendicular section across this ridge of mountain, the nucleous of which, or the internal strata, were the object of our search. . . .

'Immediately after which we found the granite under the alpine schistus. . . .

'In matters of science, curiosity gratified begets not indolence, but new desires. We now wished to see the extent of that granite which we had found; and whether it was one continued mass of granite to the River Dee, where perhaps nothing but granite mountains are to be found, at least where chiefly those abound. We had hitherto made the Duke's hunting-lodge in Glen Tilt our head-quarters. His Grace now proposed to move us farther into the wilderness, and also to entertain us with the deer-hunting in his forest. We travelled up the Tilt, crossed the Tarf which runs into the Tilt, and came to the other hunting seat at Fealar, the most removed, I believe, of any in Britain from the habitations of men. Here we were near the summit of the country, where the water runs into the three great rivers Tay, Spey and Dee. The Duke was successful in killing three harts and one hind, all in excellent condition; and our curiosity was gratified in finding both the granite and alpine schistus in this summit of the Highlands, between Glen More and Glen Beg.

'The Duke's party proposed returning through the forest by the hills which are to the north of Glen Tilt, and we willingly accompanied them, as this was the chief part remaining to be surveyed. . . .

'Upon the south side of this ridge, which separated these two parallel valleys of Tilt and Tarf, we have already seen that the alpine strata were at the bottom of the hill, superincumbent upon the granite which composes the body of the mountain. . . .

'But here we are to draw a very different conclusion from other naturalists, who, seeing the schistus on each side of this ridge of mountain, superincumbent on the granite, would necessarily conclude that the stratified schistus had been formed upon the granite and in its present place. On the contrary, the schistus strata having been originally formed in a horizontal direction, the granite certainly interposed among these broken and displaced strata, must be considered as posterior to those strata, notwithstanding that these are found superincumbent on the granite. . . .

'From all that we have seen there is reason to conclude that the granite, although continuing upon the north side of the Tilt, is not continued without interruption, or mixture of the Alpine schistus, to the granite country of the Dee.'

Reference is then made to various intrusions of porphyry, a rock which 'does not differ from granite in the substances of which it is composed, but in the manner of its composition'.

On another day the schistus exposures of the River Garry were examined. Here Hutton and Clerk had 'the satisfaction to discover no less than eleven or twelve or those porphyry dykes intersecting the strata, but sometimes so obliquely, that it is difficult to distinguish them from a parallel bed.

'Thus our alpine country consists of indurated or erected strata of slate, gneiss, and limestone, broken, and injected with granite and porphyry'.

Comparison is then drawn between the granite and porphyry veins of the Highlands, sometimes concordant with the bedding of the schistus, sometimes discordant, and the whinstone intrusions of the Midland Valley. '*Whatever be the materials in these two cases, Nature acts upon the same principle*'.

Hutton concludes his Chapter IV with a few pages in 'regard to the operation of water upon the surface of this alpine country'. He is mainly concerned with the 'stupendous gap' that the Tay 'has gradually, in the course of time, hollowed out' in the schistus of the Highland Border at Dunkeld. He has also some notes on the alluvial terraces of the same district.

The only reference to design that we find in the chapter is contained in its last sentence: 'The continual tendency of those operations, natural to the surface of the earth, is to diminish the heights of mountains, to form plains below, and to provide soil for the growth of plants'.

Chapter 10*b*

HUTTON'S CHAPTER V OF VOLUME III 'OBSERVATIONS MADE IN A JOURNEY TO THE SOUTH ALPINE PARTS OF SCOTLAND IN THE YEAR 1786'

Hutton's Chapter V, like his Chapter IV, deals with an excursion already introduced in our Chapter 5. Its first line dates it as having been written up in 1786; but a long footnote further on was added in 1788 to draw attention to Sir James Hall's more detailed traverse of that year—also referred to in our Chapter 5.

'In harvest 1786', says Hutton, 'I set out with Mr Clerk of Eldin, who now entered warmly into the investigation; and having in view to examine also the granite of Arran, we went by Glasgow. But finding it too late in the year for exploring the mountainous region of that island we contented ourselves with making a circuit of the coast round the shires of Ayr and Galloway.

'In this tour, we had opportunity of observing the disorders or accidents of the coal and sandstone strata upon the coast of Ayrshire. . . . The dykes at Skelmorlie are remarkable.

'I had only seen granite in three places of this whole southern region, viz., at Buncle Edge in Berwickshire on the east, at Loch Doon in Ayrshire on the west, and Mount Criffel near Dumfries on the south: At Loch Doon I had formerly seen the junction of the granite and the alpine strata, about the middle of the loch; but the exposure was small and did not reveal age relationship. 'I was in great hopes of finding much of this junction upon the coast of the sea, where the agitation of the water and the attrition of the stones makes distinct sections of rocks'. Now, as he drove along past Maybole, Girvan and Ballantrae, 'I could obtain no certain information of the existence of granite anywhere in form of rock, although much of this stone in detached pieces, worn round by attrition or decay, is found both in the shire of Ayr and Galloway'. Hutton recognised these granite boulders as having 'certainly come from the granite mountains at the head of Loch Doon.

'The coal and sandstone strata are to be found no farther than Girvan, where they terminate, and the schistus appears upon the shore, in going towards Ardmillan Hill, stretching [striking] into the sea.'

The Ballantrae whinstone beyond Ardmillan is recorded, but, of course, as subterraneous, not submarine, lavas; and the coastal strip of sandstone at the village is correctly compared (wonderful to relate) with Dumfries Permian rather than Skelmorlie Old Red.

'The second ridge beyond Ballantrae is composed of the true alpine stone of schistus much erected or on edge, rising to the north-west and stretching south-west, as it commonly does; and this continues throughout all Galloway to Portpatrick on the one hand and Dumfries on the other, except where it may be occasionally interrupted by granite, porphyry or whinstone. . . .

'All the rivers of Galloway, like that of Girvan in the shire of Ayr, appear to carry granite in rolling it from the higher ground'—Hutton makes no suggestion here of possible help from glaciers of the past. 'We therefore concluded that there must be some great mass of granite in the mountainous part, as I knew there was at the head of Loch Doon, on the other side. . . .

'We had not gone many miles from Newton Stewart, until we observed most unequivocal marks of the vicinity of the granite country; this was the abundance of granite rolled in the rivers. Then looking up towards the mountains, we observed one which corresponded perfectly with that idea; this is Cairns Muir [Cairnsmore of Fleet], a great round mountain, exposed immediately to view from that part of the road upon the coast. Therefore being now determined, we put up our chaise at the village of Ferrytown [Creetown], and procured horses and a guide to conduct us through the muir in persuit of the object we had in view. . . .

'Our satisfaction was complete, in finding almost every means of information that we could desire. In approaching to this place, we had the pleasure to perceive detached pieces of rock composed of both granite and the common schistus of this country; and in this composition it appeared that granite was the invading and the schistus the invaded body'. Still, minute examination in these mountains was laborious owing to the prevalence of a 'mossy covering... a serious subject of regret'. What was wanted was ready-washed exposures, like those of Glen Tilt, 'either in the bed of a river, or upon the seashore. . . . We saw, however, enough to describe upon principle what we here had learned'. Where 'the general mass might be considered as of granite, this did not hinder that in places there was as much of the schistus as of the including granite. In some places insulated pieces of schistus appeared included with the granite rock; in other places again, the granite showed only veins which traversed the schistus in different directions. Though I had entertained the most flattering expectation of being gratified with the junction of those two bodies, it was not possible to conceive an appearance more perfectly calculated to remove every doubt, or to command belief, with regard to an operation which perhaps never can be seen. . . .

'Being thus fully satisfied with the day's adventure we returned at dark to the village, and set out next day on our journey round the coast'. Arrived at the Dee the party found well exposed porphyry dykes. (These Geikie in a note connects with the great granite mass at Kirkcudbright.)

Leaving this town, 'we travelled a road which perhaps was never passed in a chaise before. We found granite alternating with schistus, but the junction was covered.' Beyond Colvend it is customary to use the strand at low tide as a road, 'nearer, easier, and far more expeditious; but this was not our object; for now the rocky shore appeared, and we had every reason to expect to find something interesting in this critical spot. We therefore left the chaise, which we had for a long way attended on foot, to find its way up the hill, while we ran with some impatience along the bottom of the sandy bay to the rocky shore which is washed by the sea, it being then low water. . . . We saw the place nearby where the granite and the schistus upon the shore must be united; but this place was bushy; and thus our fears and expectations remained for a moment in suspense. But breaking through the bushes and briars, and climbing up the rocky bank, if we did not see the opposition of the granite to the side of the erected strata so much as we would have wished, we saw something that was much more satisfactory, and to the purpose of our expedition. This was the granite superimposed upon the ends of those broken strata or erected schisti. . . .

'But even this view of things, decisive as it was, did not fill up the measure of our satisfaction, which was to be still farther gratified with the only possible appearance which could now remain, in order to complete the proof with every species of evidence which the nature of things could admit of. For here we found the granite not only involving the terminations of the broken and elevated strata, but also interjected among the strata, in descending among them like a mineral vein, and terminating in a thread where it could penetrate no farther. . . .

'Upon the whole, we may now conclude, that, without seeing the granite actually in a fluid state, we have every demonstration possible of this fact; that is to say, of granite having been forced to flow, in a state of fusion among strata broken by a subterranean force, and distorted in every manner and degree. . . .

'I have been the more anxious upon this subject, as I was long doubtful with regard to granite; . . . I was uncertain if granite should be considered as a stratification of matter collected at the bottom of the sea, and afterwards consolidated by fusion in its place, or if it should be considered as a mass of subterraneous lava, which had been made to flow in the manner of our whinstone or basaltes. . . .

'I have now only further to add, that I do not pretend to say that there is no stratified granite'.

Comparison of Strata and Structure in the three main divisions of Scotland

Having said all he wants to about granitic intrusion in the western part of the Southern Uplands, Hutton discusses possible relationships between the Alpine schistus of the Southern Uplands and that of the Highlands. He points out differences. The hard stratified rocks in the Southern Uplands are clearly indurated sandstone, while those in the Highlands are 'granulated quartz', in which Hutton has not detected detrital grains. Also, the soft strata in the Southern Uplands are devoid of conspicuous mica, while those in the Highlands abound in it. He then points to a notable resemblance. The schistus of both districts has been intensely folded with N.E.–S.W. 'stretch' or strike. Hutton feels certain that the movements thus registered were of the same general age—a good suggestion, whether right or wrong.

Here we come to a difficult part of the subject. Hutton claims that the relatively gentle folding of the Coal Measures of the Midland Valley shows some tendency to N.E.–S.W. strike—which is perfectly true, for instance, in the Edinburgh coalfield. He goes on to say that 'this would indicate the action of one great cause, or a certain generality in that operation by which the bottom of the sea had been erected into the place of land'. I do not think he can possibly have meant that the for-the-most-part gentle folding of the Coal Measures was contemporaneous with the strong folding of the schistus on either side, but merely that the two phenomena show 'a certain generality' in their direction.

Hutton then proceeds to say: 'It will now be allowed that the notion of primitive, secondary and tertiary mountains, which has of late so much prevailed among philosophers or naturalists, is not well founded'. By this he clearly means that what Pallas in 1777 called 'Primitive' has, through metamorphism, been derived from the 'Secondaries' and 'Tertiaries' of past ages. We have already noted that Pallas' philosophy was more evolutionary, and Hutton's more reactionary. To this extent modern geology has followed Pallas; but for many purposes it employs uniformitarianism as a very valuable approximate guide in conducting its researches. Hutton concludes with the following statement of his 'system in which the old continents forming in the bottom of the sea; and a system in which the subterranean power of fire, or heat, cooperates with the action of water upon the surface of the Earth, for the restoration of that order of things which is necessarily lost in the maintaining of a living world—a world beautifully calculated for the growth of plants and nourishment of animals'.

It is significant that here, as in his Chapter IV, Hutton has reserved his 'moral' argument for the final sentence.

Chapter 10c

HUTTON'S CHAPTER VI OF VOLUME III 'A COMPARISON OF M. DE SAUSSURE'S OBSERVATIONS IN THE ALPS, WITH THOSE MADE UPON THE GRANITE MOUNTAINS OF SCOTLAND'

Most of De Saussure's observations on the relations of granite to schistus were carried out in the Mont Blanc district, under much more difficult conditions, human and geological, than those attending Hutton's explorations in Glen Tilt and Galloway.

In Hutton's words: 'I had longed to see the continuation of de Saussure's *Voyages dans les Alpes* [Vol. I, 1779; now Vol. II, 1786], but it was not till I had written an account of our second expedition to the granite mountains of this country that I received it. The reader will guess the impatience I felt to see what interesting observations this able naturalist had made with regard to the junction of the granite and schistus in the Alps. I have every reason to be satisfied with M. de Saussure; but the success of his labours did not come up to my sanguine expectation or my wishes. It is but in few places that this junction of those different bodies is to be perceived; at least, our author, though carefully looking for this occurrence, met with it rarely. In having been so fortunate myself, I perhaps expected too much from those alpine scenes, where the difficulty of making the proper observations increases with the grandeur of the subject. . . .

'It is true indeed, that our author's view is in some measure diametrically opposite to mine. . . . I think myself fortunate in having written the histories of my mineral observations, before I had read the second volume in which those of M. de Saussure are recorded'.

Here Hutton would have done well to stop. Instead he continues with a long dissertation, including full measure of quotations—the whole very hazy and unrewarding.

Chapter 10*d*

HUTTON'S CHAPTER VII OF VOLUME III 'THEORY CONFIRMED BY OBSERVATIONS MADE UPON THE PYRENEAN MOUNTAINS'

Hutton decides, in a mercifully short chapter, to compare the geological laws of Scotland with those of the Pyrenees, so as to test their generality. For data concerning the latter region he consults an *Essai sur la Minéralogie des Monts Pyrénées,* the fruit of nearly 40 years of research by the Abbé Palassou. It was published in 1782 under the patronage of the Royal Academy of Sciences. There he finds descriptions of composition and consolidation of strata comparable with what he has given in his account of Scotland. So far he feels no need to introduce a new law into his *Theory*.

Hutton continues: 'We now come to that great stumbling block of mineral system, the vertical direction of the strata, or the changes which those bodies have undergone in departing from their original horizontal posture. . . .

'Among strata, therefore, upon which [according to the Huttonian *Theory*] the subterranean power has acted much, the vertical and horizontal positions should be considered as the two extreme states in which those bodies may be found; and the inclined position which includes an indefinite variety, or a perfect gradation, should be that which must commonly appear'.

Hutton gathers from Palassou that such a variety of dips is common for the Pyrenean strata, and that northward dips are characteristic of those strata that lie north of an axial granitic range in the mountains. From this flimsy evidence he concludes that the granite has been intruded below the associated strata, lifting them upon its back. He does not mention that Palassou thinks that the inclined dips are original, and that the granite underlies the associated strata because it is older than they are. Geikie in his notes points out that Palassou's views about original dips are absurd. Hutton, in totally disregarding them, seems to think that his contemporary readers are aware of current discussions, and can be left to form their own opinions upon this particular matter.

'We have now only further to observe that the mountains, according to [the Huttonian] theory, should have been much degraded. . . . The immense quantity of sand and water-worn gravel, with which the lower country of the north of this alpine ridge is covered, must be joined as affording the most complete evidence of that fact'.

Chapter 10*e*

HUTTON'S CHAPTER VIII OF VOLUME III 'AN ILLUSTRATION OF THE THEORY FROM THE NATURAL HISTORY OF CALABRIA'

After having written Volume III up to this point, Hutton read an account of the famous Calabrian earthquake of 1783, published by de Dolomieu in 1784. According to custom, he quotes from it freely; and the following is just a short abstract:

'Calabria, in the foot of Italy, has almost everywhere a granite foundation. The focus of the earthquake lay below this apparently unshakable floor. There are at the surface no vestiges of volcanoes, . . . no lavas, no tuffs, no scoriae of any sort'. It will be remembered that de Dolomieu was a Vulcanist convert from Wernerian Neptunism; but he was no Plutonist, nor, as we shall see, a Uniformitarian. At any rate his finding that the granite underlay associated Alpine strata was enough to convince him that it was the oldest rock exposed in the district.

Let us see what Hutton has to say in regard to this last point: 'It may be asked how far the appearances here described are explainable in all their parts by the present Theory, or are perfectly corresponding with those from whence the theory of granite injections had been formed. In all the places where I have seen the granite and the alpine schisti meet together, I have found clear demonstration of the granite masses having been injected in a fluid state among the broken and disordered strata. It now remains for M. le Chevalier de Dolomieu to say how far he found similar appearances in those places where he has given us to understand that there is a mixture of those different things, and where in all probability some appearances in those places may be found by which this important question might be decided.

'We now come to the second part proposed, which is to compare with this natural history of Calabria the present Theory respecting the degradation of the surface of the Earth, by the decay of rocks and the attrition of bodies moved by water flowing in the rivers and agitated with the wind'. Here we pass from consideration of ancient consolidated rocks to Quaternary events which have built up an extensive Plain of loose materials, hundreds of feet thick. The solid mountains rise steeply behind to emaciated summits, which have supplied the debris constituting the thick body of the Plain: namely, 'quartzose sand, pebbles, grey and white clay, and grains of felspar and mica coming from the decomposition of the granite. The whole is mixed with shells and fragments of marine organisms . . . including a great quantity of superb sea-urchins'.

Of course this description of great accumulations resulting from comparatively recent erosion is very much to Hutton's taste; but de Dolomieu's hypothesis of how the deposit came into position involves catastrophes on a much larger scale than humanity has experienced during historic times. 'These masses of matter', de Dolomieu says, 'are unrelated to one another, and unconsolidated; they appear to be a deposit of the sea, driven by westerly gales of a magnitude not experienced in our own times. They seem to be derived from the local summits along with what inundation has brought from a distance, all piled up and battered at the foot of the mountains'.

To show that catastrophic deluges need not be invoked, Hutton offers two possible alternatives: one of them involves earth-movement; the other dispenses with such movement, but suggests that de Dolomieu's marine shells have been derived by subaerial erosion from the fossiliferous Alpine strata of the mountains. This last was a bold suggestion, and one is not surprised to learn on Geikie's authority that it has been set aside by later Italian geologists.

Chapter 10f

HUTTON'S CHAPTER IX OF VOLUME III 'AN EXAMINATION OF THE MINERAL HISTORY OF THE ISLAND OF ARRAN'

After meeting certain difficulties during the summer of 1787, Hutton decided to go alone in August to study the granite-schistus contact which he was certain he would find in Arran. On hearing of this project, John Clerk, junior, volunteered to accompany him. The two sailed from Saltcoats, and, when within a mile or so of Holy Isle, they began to see intrusive contacts. The ensuing account in his Chapter IX was drawn up in essence the same year, before, as G. W. Tyrrell has pointed out, Hutton stumbled on to the Jedburgh exposure of unconformity (Chapter 6). The draft, however, cannot have been handed over to Hutton's amanuensis before 1790, as we shall presently see.

All that Hutton knew before he started was the beautiful Alpine scenery of the northern part of Arran, as viewed from a distance, the presence of granite in its mountains; and the occurrence of some coal and limestone elsewhere: still, this was enough to tempt him to test in it 'the Theory of the Earth which had been formed from that of other parts'. He found in the small compass of the island, what might 'be considered as a specimen of our earth'.

Eventually he divided the island into three main Parts, 1–3, with two subdivisions, Parts 4 and 5, recognisable in Part 3. Thus: Part 1 is the granite outcrop; Part 2 the schistus outcrop; Part 3 the sandstone, etc., outcrop; while Part 4 is a subdivision of Part 3 copiously intruded by porphyry and petuntze (an Italian name for felsite); and Part 5 another subdivison of Part 3, in this case copiously intruded by whin or basalt in the form of sills. Whin or basalt dykes, especially well seen at low tide along the south coast, were treated, not as limited to any particular part, but as a late feature of the island as a whole.

Part 1. In his description of the Arran granite, Hutton draws attention to the 'extremely deep valleys' which had been 'excavated' in its substance; and he mentions as a feature of Glen Rosa 'a charming picture of lofty mountains going into decay, apparently without a purpose'. Another prominent feature of the granite region is layer jointing, which at a distance looks like stratification. 'In examining more closely into the matter, it is, I think,' says Hutton, 'sufficiently evident that this regular decay or apparent stratification of those masses of granite is only occasioned by the regular contraction or basaltic cracking of the mass in cooling; and it is the influence of the atmosphere which, insinuating itself into these invisible cracks, is the cause of that apparent stratification which in certain views is very imposing.' This is an excellent deduction, though probably the layered jointing should be referred to comparatively late removal of cover by erosion rather than to cooling. In describing the mineral features of the rock, Hutton emphasises the peculiar character of its quartz, 'transparent and much approaching to the crystalline'. The transparency contrasts with the 'milky hue natural to that of granite in general', for instance at Aberdeen or Portsoy. (Though Hutton did not know it, the Arran granite is of Tertiary age, in the modern sense of that term, whereas the other granites of his acquaintance are much more ancient.)

Parts 1–2. Search for an exposed junction of granite and schistus had led Hutton to Arran. He was abundantly rewarded. Here is his own account of his first success, after some fruitless attempts from Brodick.

'I set out on horseback for Loch Ranza; with a view to investigate the same object by the way, as well as to examine the north end of the island, where I knew the coal and slate were worked near the shore. Upon this road I observed that the North Sanox river, which I had crossed in entering the schistus district to the north, runs nearly in the junction of the schistus and the granite mountains, the characters of which are very distinguishable to the view. I then went forward, but in returning I quitted my horse, and went over the mosses and muir towards the heads of that North Sanox river which here divides into two streams. Here I had the satisfaction to find the immediate junction of the schistus with the granite in the solid rock, exposed perfectly to view, and that in both of these rivulets, a little way above their junction.

'Nothing can be more evident than that here the schistus had been broken and invaded by the granite. . . .

'Not contented with this view of those two alpine bodies, in that jaunt which I had taken alone, I wished to give Mr Clerk the same satisfaction, and also to see this example from the summit of a hill as well as in the bottom of a valley, a good opportunity here occurred to make the trial; for to the south of Goatfield [Goatfell] there rises a shoulder, which may be considered either as the summit of a hill or the basis of that mountain', and 'we knew that the line of junction which we were in quest of, must run over the top of this shoulder or mountain. One day, therefore, when disappointed in seeking this junction on the Cataract* rock, which with the fair weather had become almost dry; and when Mr Clerk had taken some drawings of several veins of granite, which traverse the schistose rock from the junction which is here no more than just out of sight, we directed our course to the summit of this hill, from whence we could look down upon the place of junction in Glen Rosa. Here we had little trouble in procuring what we wanted, and found the most satisfactory evidence of the point we sought to ascertain.

'For though, by reason of the covering of moss and vegetation, we had but a very interrupted view of this object, the immediate junction of the granite and schistus, which here appears in many places upon the summits of bare rock standing up among the heath and moss, yet we had every other reason to be perfectly satisfied with what we saw; and having once got hold of the clew, or catched the scent, we traced back with more animation than could have been expected from such an innocent chase, the object of our investigation, all the way to the very place from which we had set out at the head of the Cataract rock. . . .

'Both upon the summit of this hill and on the top of the Cataract rock in time of drought, may be seen great veins of granite traversing the schistus, and ramifying in all directions. It was here that I procured a specimen of this, which I have had conveyed to Edinburgh, though weighing about 600 pounds. . . .

'This great body of granite had been actually in a state of fusion by means of subterraneous heat. Here is a matter of fact, or physical truth, which I hope will be found to have been concluded upon just grounds, and may then be employed in examining the various theories of the Earth'.

Part 2. The second district to be now considered consists of alpine schistus, and is most immediately connected with the first. It

* The Cataract lies on what is now called the Cnocan Burn, a little downstream from a milldam.

lies mostly to the north of the first district; but it also surrounds the great body of granite with a skirt. . . .

'It is a hard slaty schistus with quartz in veins and masses'.

Parts 2–3. Hutton tells us: 'The immediate connection of the alpine schistus with the strata of the low country is an object which I have long looked for, I may almost say in vain. I expected to have seen it in entering the Grampian mountains, both by the Ammon [Almond] and the Tay, but I was disappointed in my expectations. . . . I have in like manner looked for it on both sides of the southern mountains of Scotland, and that in several places without receiving any satisfaction on that subject. In the island of Arran I have sought it carefully without finding it in a place where I thought it was certainly to be found; and I found it in a place where I had not thought almost of looking for it. . . .

'Loch Ranza at the north end of the island is properly within the Alpine schistus, but, in tracing the shore, upon the east side of the loch or bay, we come to the extremity of this schistus district. Here the first thing that occurs is the immediate junction of the inclined strata of schistus and the other strata which here appear to be a composition of sandstone and limestone; these strata are equally inclined with the schistus, but in the opposite direction. Those two different kinds of strata rise to meet each other; they are somewhat confused at the immediate junction; but some of the sandstone or calcareous strata overlap the ends of the alpine schistus'. Hutton meant to publish a drawing which he took in his notebook.

The unconformable strata belong to the cornstone division of the Upper Old Red Sandstone; and there has been marked chemical erosion of the underlying schistus—here phyllite. This has led to the sands and limestones penetrating irregularly, on a small scale, a few feet down into what is mainly schistus. This is what Hutton means when he says the immediate junction is 'somewhat confused'. I remember how impressed I was, on visiting the exposure in 1926, to find this evidence of Hutton's close examination. The phenomenon has been compared by J. E. Richey (*Ardnamurchan Mem.,* 1930, p. 35) with the chemical corrosion one often finds at the base of Triassic cornstones in the Hebrides; and the existence of 'Dalradian schists strongly impregnated and cemented by calcareous material' at Hutton's Loch Ranza locality has also been noted by S. I. Tomkeieff (*Geol. Mag.,* 1953, p. 407).

Part 3. 'The third or general district is that which, among our modern naturalists, is termed the secondary or tertiary masses of our globe'. 'The stratification of this mass is too evident to be disputed; and the origin of this body from the various known matter deposited by natural operations at the bottom of the sea, is acknowledged by everybody.

'This stratified body consists' of: sandstone, in general red; puddingstone; marl; marine fossiliferous limestone; and coal—the last in two or three vertical seams of blind or smokeless seams at the north end of the island. 'This mass of strata, in general around the island, is horizontal, or not greatly changed from its natural position, except where it comes to be in connection with the alpine bodies, or otherwise effected by the bodies which remain now to be considered.'

Parts 3–4. As stated above, the fourth district is part of the third, distinguished only by an abundance of porphyry and petuntze sills. It has therefore no definite boundary.

Part 4. Within the fourth district, at Corriecravie on the west coast, Hutton found a mountain of porphyry, two or three miles wide. It forms a 'mountain of one mass, and breaking or separating into great blocks precisely like the granite. . . . But this mass by its internal structure is more properly a porphyry, as it has a general ground, and as this ground is maculated with the crystalline or transparent quartz and the felt-spath. I would therefore term it as a granite porphyry, as containing almost the same materials as granite, only in a porphyry form'. This, with the sequel, amounts to a recognition that the sills of District 4 have close petrographical similarities with the boss of Part 1.

Hutton did not find at shore level any exposed contact of the Corriecravie granite-porphyry and the associated sediments; and he left it an open question as to whether the granite-porphyry should be regarded as a repetition of the granite of Part 1 or as an example of the porphyries in Part 4. Among other examples of the latter he mentions the Shiskin porphyry on the west coast and the Holy Island petuntze on the east. He has no doubt that the Arran porphyries and petuntzes are varieties of the same material and that they pass into one another. 'Though', he says, 'I did not see the immediate connection of the granite porphyry with the strata, this is not the case with the petuntze-porphyry. I have seen the most convincing and unquestionable proof that, on both sides of the island of Arran, this last body has been made to break and invade the strata of sandstone and marl, in every conceivable manner'.

Parts 4–5. In as much as the petuntze bodies have a strong tendency to follow bedding, and to develop cross-jointing of columnar type, they may very conveniently be regarded along with their basaltic analogues as 'subterraneous lavas'. They differ in 'wanting that feruginous matter which characterises the common sort of whinstone of this country'. Hutton also recognised (wonderful to relate!) that some of the Arran basalts carry minute clear idiomorphic quartz crystals such as he had found in the granite and granite-porphyry of the island (his reference is p. 216).

Part 5. 'Having shown the affinity of the porphyry with the whinstone which characterizes the southern district, and having observed that the porphyry is found to have broken and invaded the strata in every supposable manner, we have only to substitute the one species of body for the other, and then the description will equally apply to both'.

Turning to dykes. Hutton finds the districts, or Parts 1–5, no longer helpful, since dykes are found everywhere in the island.

'From the many whinstone dykes or veins which traverse the strata upon the shore of the shire of Ayr, I had reason to expect something of the same kind in the island of Arran. But the number and complexity of those dykes, which we found upon all the shores of the island, surpassed anything which I had imagined or could well suppose, from what I had ever seen before. . . .

'Not only is the granite "dyked", to use the miner's term, by whinstone, it is also traversed in like manner by petuntze'. Between the glens of Rosa on the west and of Corrie 'on the east, the mass of granite is here traversed perpendicularly by a dyke which is more properly petuntze than whinstone. Our curiosity in examining this dyke tempted us to slip down this place, in descending the mountain into the high Cory Glen, an idea which could not have entered the head of any sober person who was not a mineralogist.'

All through, Hutton appreciates intersections as establishing age-relations. For instance in the south, he records sills cut by dykes, and in the north, granite similarly treated.

Pitchstones. Hutton next turns to certain remarkable sills and dykes of 'natural glass', the world-famous pitchstones of Arran. He even notes in them 'an appearance of a fibrous substance floating in the transparent mass; and is no other than a crystallization of some of the materials. An appearance similar to this is always found in our common glasshouse pots, when the green bottle glass is not perfectly vitrified by sufficient fusion, or when it has undergone some change in cooling. . . .

'This glass of Arran would appear to be nearly porphyry' with 'maculae of felt-spath and quartz or crystal'.

Hutton then compares the geology of Arran with that of Islay, Jura, Mull and Iona, based on letters from Abraham Mills read to the Royal Society of London in 1790; and follows up with an account of local coastal erosion. The most interesting item here is Hutton's telling of how he had been informed by Rudolf Erik Raspe of a coal under whinstone on the south coast of Mull. Thus we learn that Hutton was at the time in touch with Raspe, one of the most active and able of the geologists of his day. Geikie in a footnote tells us:

'The Mr Raspe above referred to had an eventful history. Born in Hanover (1737), he wrote on mineralogical and geological subjects, was charged with peculation, escaped from prison to England, obtained some mining employment in Cornwall, travelled over England and Scotland searching for possible mines, and finally died while on some similar journey in Ireland. He wrote and published anonymously the well-known *Adventures of Baron Munchausen*, and he is said to have been the prototype of Dousterswivel, Scott's "tramping philosopher" in *The Antiquary*—where "Dr Hutton" is referred to by name as the "celebrated geologist".'

Lyell, in his *Principles of Geology* has a good word for Raspe, especially in regard to a 1763 account of new islands in the Mediterranean, including possible correlation with earthquakes. This book of Raspe's furnishes a very valuable review of the teachings of Hooke, Ray, Moro, Buffon and others—with special admiration expressed for Hooke's hypothesis apart from the latter's suggestion that many convulsions accompanied Noah's deluge.

Finally Hutton brings his Volume III to a close with the claim that his 'Theory of the Earth . . . is confirmed from the history of Arran'.

Before, however, we say goodbye to Hutton's Chapter IX, let us attempt a solution of a puzzle of long standing. How was it that Hutton made no mention of two of the most obvious assets of this treasure island of geology? One is the 25 ft. raised beach, the other, the dispersal of great granite boulders. It is inconceivable that he could have overlooked them.

The eroded platform of the raised beach girdles the island, backed by an old sea cliff, with caves worthy of an industrious spider and a king in hiding. Hutton cannot have been other than delighted with this clear evidence of interchange between land and sea; but the beach is virtually horizontal within the limits of the island, and so does not answer the question: Has the land risen or the sea withdrawn?

As for the granite erratics, they must have tempted Hutton to compare them with the granite erratics of the Mont Blanc district; but he didn't dare to conjure up Arran glaciers where today palms grow in the open thanks to the beneficence of what we used to call the Gulf Stream.

Chapter 11

1795-1797
THE END

AFTER PUBLISHING in 1795 Volumes I and II of his *Theory of the Earth* in book form, Hutton set about adding final touches to his *Principles of Agriculture,* which we have dealt with in our own Chapter 2. For the rest let us reproduce Playfair's account given in his own words:

'The period, however, was now not far distant, which was to terminate the exercise of a mind of such singular activity, and of such ardour in the pursuit of knowledge. Not long after the time we are speaking of, Dr Hutton was again attacked by the same disorder from which he had already made so remarkable recovery. He was again saved from the danger that immediately threatened him, but his constitution had materially suffered, and nothing could restore him to his former strength. He recovered, indeed, so far as to amuse himself with study, and with the conversation of his friends, and even to go on with the work on agriculture, which was nearly completed. He was, however, confined entirely to the house; and in the course of the winter 1796–7, he became gradually weaker, was extremely emaciated, and suffered much pain, but still retained the full activity and acuteness of his mind. He constantly employed himself in reading and writing, and was particularly pleased with the third and fourth volumes of Saussure's *Voyages dans les Alpes,* which reached him in the course of that winter, and became the last study of one eminent geologist, as they were the last work of another. On Saturday the 26th of March he suffered a good deal of pain, but, nevertheless employed himself in writing, and particularly in noting down his remarks on some attempts that were then making towards a new mineralogical nomenclature [possibly in Werner's *New Theory of the Formation of Veins,* 1791]. In the evening he was seized with a shivering, and his uneasiness continuing to increase, he sent for his friend Mr Russel, who attended him as his surgeon. Before he could possibly arrive all medical assistance was in vain: Dr Hutton had just strength left to stretch out his hand to him, and immediately expired'.

ADDENDUM

Hutton was buried in the historic churchyard of Greyfriars, Edinburgh, where, in the reign of Charles I, the momentous Solemn League and Covenant was signed, 1643. Strangely enough his grave bore no inscription until the 150th anniversary of his death when Sir John Falconer, Lord Provost of the City, unveiled a tablet at the site. The ceremony was part of the commemoration organised in 1947 by the Royal Society of Edinburgh.

It seems fitting to add a few words to indicate how far the ideas set out in Hutton's *Theory of the Earth* live after him. In tracing their early struggle for existence we draw mainly on the publications of three geologists additional to Playfair and Geikie.

(1) Robert Jameson (1774–1854) was born in Leith. *Robinson Crusoe* and Cook's *Voyages* had much to do in deciding the course of his life. In keeping with this we find that, during his schooldays, he was a notorious truant, pursuing insects and other living creatures instead of the wisdom of the classroom. For a time he prepared for surgery at Edinburgh University; and in 1792–3 he took a natural history course under Professor Walker. Between 1794 and 1799 he travelled extensively in the Scottish Isles, and was able to publish his well known mineralogical account of them in 1800—in Wernerian terms. This same year he set out for Freiberg to perfect his knowledge of the Wernerian school. He returned in 1804, and was appointed to the Chair of Natural History, opportunely left vacant by Professor Walker's death. This post he held for 50 years, during much of which he acted as leader of a very confident and vocal party of loyal Wernerians. There resulted an unusually bitter assault upon the Plutonists marshalled under Playfair and Hall. Apart from this, Jameson added to the intellectual stature of Edinburgh by developing a museum, which has since been adopted by the nation, by much increasing opportunities for scientific publication, and by

attracting many outstanding students. In this last connexion the brilliant zoologist Edward Forbes said of him: 'not even his famous master, the eloquent and illustrious Werner, could equal him in the genesis of investigators'. On his death he was honoured with a public funeral.

(2) W. H. Fitton (1780–1861) was one of Jameson's gifted students who later went over to the Huttonian ranks. He did valuable stratigraphical work on the Cretaceous of southern England, and served for a time as President of the Geological Society of London. We introduce him here on account of his close knowledge of the history of geology in its formative days. In 1839 he published a famous anonymous essay in the *Edinburgh Review* dealing with Lyell's *Elements of Geology* and the Huttonian *Theory of the Earth.* It supplies a particularly valuable discussion of Ami Boué's insufficient acknowledgement of Hutton's priority in relation to Plutonic geology.

(3) Ami Boué (1794–1881) was another of Jameson's pupils who presently went over to the other side. He was born in Hamburg of Franco-Swiss parents, and was sent to Edinburgh for a medical education. Having graduated M.D. in 1816, he roamed widely over Scotland, botanising and geologising. In Paris for a time, he produced in book-form an *Essai Geologique sur l'Ecosse*. The date is probably 1820. At any rate Boué tells us that he had to make extensive alterations in his proofs on the appearance in 1819 of James Macculloch's *Description of the Western Isles of Scotland;* and on another page he refers to G. B. Greenough's 'new geological map' of England, which appeared in 1820 (following Smith's masterpiece of 1815).

The *Essai* is in the main a crowded compilation dealing with Scottish geology; and the indebtedness of this part to Macculloch, 'historian of Scotland's volcanic deposits', is clearly acknowledged. Then follow unexpectedly detailed comparative studies of the geologies of England, Ireland, France and north Germany; after which on p. 393 the question is posed: '*What is the origin of the Scottish formation?*' Actually Boué had dealt with many aspects of this question on preceding pages—but he has still points to add. In after years Boué played a great part in unravelling the geology of France and Germany.

Some few of Hutton's successors at the time of his death were complete Huttonians, accepting his teaching in all directions. Playfair was such a one; but others agreed only upon particular points. Hall, for instance, believed not in the uniformitarian erosion of valleys; whereas Desmarest right up to his death in 1815 disbelieved in the igneous origin of granite, though he had done so much to establish such an origin in the case of basalt. Accordingly our further discussion will be arranged under a few subject headings.

Religion.—In the presentation of his *Theory,* Hutton mingled promiscuously his ideas of design in nature with his direct observations of geological phenomena. Playfair's *Illustrations,* 1802, clarified the situation immensely by showing that the *Theory* could be successfully rewritten without reference to any hypothesis of design.

Volcanic Phenomena.—Although Hutton developed his igneous interpretation of whinstone independently, he admitted that the Vulcanists of the Continent had already reached the same conclusion by what we may call a uniformitarian comparison of the products of active and extinct volcanoes. Hutton evidently thought that this anticipation made his discovery of little importance; but, as a matter of history, the origin of whinstone was a major subject of dispute in the Edinburgh battle that followed his death—and his igneous interpretation won the day, largely on local evidence. On the other hand his separation of 'proper lavas' from 'subterraneous lavas' was less successful, for he was mistaken in allocating *all* Scottish whins to the latter class. Connected with this, his claim that amygdales are not the infillings of vesicles had soon to be abandoned (*cf.* Boué, p. 394).

In 1802 the Continental Neptunists received a great blow when D'Aubuisson de Voisins (1769–1819), Leopold von Buch (1774–1852) and Alexander von Humboldt (1769–1859), Werner's three most distinguished pupils, became Vulcanists. The two former owed their conversion to visiting Auvergne. These dramatic somersaults had at first comparatively little effect in Scotland, where for long Jameson proved unbending.

Let us pass on to the appearance of Boué's *Essai,* 1820, which, by the way, was tactfully dedicated to his old master. We find in it ten formations listed in the geological make up of Scotland: (1) Granite; (2) Gneiss; (3) Mica-schist; (4) Porphyry; (5) Chlorite-schist and

Quartzite; (6) Greywacke; (7) Red Sandstone, at first without coal, later with; (8) Hebridean Limestones and Sandstones, with *Gryphaea;* (9) Volcanics; (10) Alluvium. Boué grouped: (1–5) as Primitive or Primordial; (6) as Transitional (we say Ordovician and Silurian); (7–8) as Secondary (we say (7) Old Red Sandstone and Carboniferous, and (8) Jurassic); (9) as Volcanic, on more than one horizon; and (10) as comparatively modern Superficial Deposits (we say Glacial and Post-glacial).

Here we are concerned only with Boué's Volcanic Formation. He divided it into two parts, both of them long previously recognised by Huttonians to be truly igneous. The younger part (later than the Jurassic, and, in Antrim later than the Chalk) is grouped about dyke-centres in Skye, Mull and Arran. Its rocks are now belatedly admitted by Boué to be indubitably igneous. The older part is contemporaneous with some of the Old Red Sandstone and Carboniferous of the Midland Valley, as in the Ochills, Pentlands, Arthur's Seat, etc. Its igneous origin was still regarded by Boué as doubtful; but the comparisons he institutes suggest that by this time, 1820, his doubts were no longer very serious. Five years later, 1825, we find Boué publishing in Jameson's *Edinburgh Philosophical Journal* the following appreciation of the position as it had by then developed.

(1) All geologists accept extinct volcanoes.
(2) Most accept Tertiary basalt as volcanic.
(3) Many accept the trap of the Secondaries.
(4) Some (including Boué) regard granite, syenite and porphyries as igneous.

Werner had died in 1817, and Fitton reminds us that Boué in the *Journal de Physique* for 1822 had already mentioned 'with evident reluctance', and 'as a truth which others may be unwilling to make public', that his death introduced an epoch for the advance of geological science in Germany. Fitton also cites, in addition to the overshadowing J. Macculloch, the following comparatively early supporters of Hutton in the Geological Society of London: A. Aiken, 1812; T. Webster, 1814; W. Conybeare and W. Buckland, 1816. 'The mass of information', he says, 'contained in the first four volumes of the Geological Society, all previous to 1817, would be sufficient, if there were no other evidence, to establish the Plutonic theory and a great part even of the development and detail of the metamorphic doctrine.'

Granite.—One readily understands special reluctance to admit the igneous origin of granite. Unlike basalt, granite never appears as a 'proper' lava in modern volcanoes. Also unlike basalt, it cannot be produced in an open crucible. Ami Boué in his *Essai* gives a long list of Scottish granites; and he recalls the Neptunian view that granite, gneiss and mica-schist constitute a succession of crystalline precipitates from an ocean of primitive composition. He notes, however, that difficulties often obscure this succession in Scotland; and he suggests that there may have been occasional recurrences of granitic deposition. He shows particular interest in granite veins, such as gave such pleasure to Hutton in 1785; but the following extract reveals how far he was prepared to go in 1820 to avoid breaking altogether with the Neptunian interpretation. In south-west Scotland he was ready to mistake hornfelsed greywacke for 'a variety of very compact and indistinct [Primitive] gneiss, . . . almost always neatly separated from' adjacent Transitional greywacke. The 'indistinct gneiss' could be regarded as practically contemporaneous with associated granite and as carrying granite veins in its own right. The Transitional greywacke he thought to be altogether later, and to be unveined. How different from Hutton's long-previous happy realisation of the truth! How different too from Boué's own description of granite intrusion in the Pyrenees which was soon to follow in the *Edinburgh Philosophical Journal* for 1823! 'Whoever', says Boué, 'has seen the beautiful series of granite veins which here [in the Pyrenees] cut, and sometimes support, the granite, will no longer doubt that the igneous origin of that rock is posterior to the slate formation. If the rock named Blaue Kuppe be a clear proof of the igneous theory respecting basalt, those places show that the true origin of granite also has been discovered by Hutton; and our respect for the views of this original thinker is increased by observing that the masses of granular limestone seem to be in close dependence upon those of granite.' Fitton has pointed out that this clear acknowledgement of Hutton's priority is the only one that Boué ever published on the subject, thus leading foreigners in later days to suppose that he was the original discoverer of the igneous intrusion of granite. I think, however, that Fitton exaggerated just a little, for foreigners of the time under consideration fairly often referred to the Plutonic school, and in all probability had a hazy notion that it originated in Edinburgh in pre-Boué days.

I cannot close this section without alluding to the fact that Hutton's ideas have continued to have opponents right up to the present day. Several living petrologists of the first rank consider: that the major granites of Scotland, France, etc., have resulted, not from intrusion of magma, but from chemical exchange between country-rock and ascending emanations; that these bodies have never been liquid *en masse;* and that their veins merely indicate that some parts at some times have been in that condition. For myself I am a Huttonian.

Metamorphism.—Boué in his Pyrenees paper, 1823, makes the following amazing mis-statement. 'Hutton', he says, 'furnished no explanation of gneiss, or of crystalline slate connected with transition slate'. He then goes on: 'The Pyrenees seem also to afford a hint of this particulaı process of nature. Gneiss is not an igneous rock', and crystalline slate may be viewed as detritus upon which 'igneous agents have acted before, after, and simultaneous with the granite eruptions, thus producing a kind of change'. The fact is that, whereas Werner held that gneiss and crystalline schist are original marine crystalline precipitates, Hutton interpreted them as having suffered Plutonic metamorphism of just the same type as Boué now contemplated. One is impressed by this revelation of the scant attention given to Hutton's *Theory* by the Jameson faction in the early days of the latter's professorship. One also sympathises with Fitton's disgust, whether exaggerated or no.

Consolidation.—Hutton regarded consolidation of sediments as an early phase of metamorphism, conditioned by joint operation of heat and pressure. Here he made some of his worst mistakes; but he did better than Werner, who imagined consolidation to be an original feature of sedimentation governed by the composition of the ocean.

Elevation.—Hutton interpreted steep dips as having been developed by earth movement, a Plutonic conception. Once more he won the day against Werner. The latter thought that steep dips were an original sedimentary feature, fixed as a result of instantaneous consolidation. De Saussure's recognition of earth movement in relation to a vertical Alpine conglomerate supplied an early confirmation of Hutton's views. Connected with his realisation of earth movement, Hutton correctly replaced Werner's universal withdrawals of oceanic waters by postulating local upheavals of land.

Dykes.—Boué in his 1820 *Essai* agreed with Hutton that the swarms of basalt dykes on the west coast of Scotland are genuinely igneous. It is, however, rather amusing that he still thought that they had been fed from above, not from below as Hutton maintained in true Plutonian fashion. Boué's conception was a hang-over from Neptunian days, when the lavas as well as the dykes were interpreted as more or less crystalline precipitates from the sea.

Scenery and Time.—Hutton is at his very best in his recognition of superficial weathering, erosion and transport as responsible for all the detail of present-day landscapes. It was here that he developed his Uniformitarian outlook. Plutonic phenomena give much less scope in this matter, for they are conducted underground out of sight—though often accompanied by correlated surface changes, such as elevation, depression or volcanic eruption. The superficial activities of sunshine, wind, rain and frost, of rivers and glaciers and of coastal waves can be examined at close quarters. These agents are attacking pre-existent landscapes that are fashioned out of heterogeneous assemblages of outcropping rocks. Their varying success is clearly determined by the superficial resistance offered by these outcrops, dependent upon the substance and position of the rocks concerned. Hutton saw that present-day scenery is not final, but is a transient phase in a long succession of sceneries, past, present and future. His treatment of river systems, in which the various tributaries flow in valleys proportioned to drainage requirements, is beyond praise. Much of his philosophy is expressed in the following two selected quotation:

> 'We must conclude at least that all the valleys are the operation of running water in the course of time. If this be granted we have but to consider the mountains as formed by the hollowing out of the valleys.'

And:

> 'The height of the mountain depends upon the solidity and strength of the stone.'

Though Guettard and Desmarest said much the same thing, it is a high tribute to Hutton's attainments that his successor Lyell, born 1797 the year of Hutton's death, took almost a lifetime to reach similar conclusions, now universally admitted. Thus we find him saying in the 1865 edition of his *Elements of Geology:*

> 'Many of the earlier geologists, and Dr Hutton among them, taught that "rivers had in general hollowed out their valleys."

> This is no doubt true of rivulets and torrents, . . . but the principal valleys in almost every great hydrographical basin in the world are of a shape and magnitude which imply that they have been due to other causes besides the mere excavating power of rivers.'

And:

> 'Professor Ramsay, and some other able geologists . . . incline, nevertheless, to the opinion that the great escarpments of the chalk may have been due to pluvial and fluviatile erosion, the sea, when it last retired, having left the secondary strata planed off at one and the same level. But this hypothesis seems to me untenable. '

Lyell at the time imagined that these escarpments had been fashioned by the sea as the land was slowly raised or lowered through the zone of breakers. Fortunately W. Whittaker two years later, 1867, was able to publish, with permission, in the *Geological Magazine* the following clear statement by Lyell of a change of mind:

> 'I have long modified my opinion on denudation, and I now agree with you in considering that the escarpments round the Weald are not inland [sea-] cliffs, as I formerly supposed, although at some points the sea may have entered through transverse valleys and modified parts of them. Two arguments, namely the fact of the escarpment of the Lower Greensand being parallel to that of the Chalk, and the fact that the sea cuts its cliffs successively through different formations and never keeps for such great distances to one formation only, are I believe unanswerable.'

In many cases Hutton recognised that a vast amount of erosion had occurred. He naturally tried to form an estimate of the time involved. Comparison of classical and modern accounts of Mediterranean coastal geography and a visit to a Roman wall in the North of England convinced him that 1,000 years in human reckoning are but as yesterday in geological time. Hutton in this matter, one of the most important discoveries of science, had predecessors, but it is generally admitted that the credit for its general acceptance is mainly due to his combination of observation and theory.